PREFACE

Introduction

Internationally, code officials recognize the need for a modern, up-to-date energy conservation code addressing the design of energy-efficient building envelopes and installation of energy-efficient mechanical, lighting and power systems through requirements emphasizing performance. The *International Energy Conservation Code®*, in this 2015 edition, is designed to meet these needs through model code regulations that will result in the optimal utilization of fossil fuel and nondepletable resources in all communities, large and small.

This code contains separate provisions for commercial buildings and for low-rise residential buildings (3 stories or less in height above grade). Each set of provisions, IECC—Commercial Provisions and IECC—Residential Provisions, is separately applied to buildings within their respective scopes. Each set of provisions is to be treated separately. Each contains a Scope and Administration chapter, a Definitions chapter, a General Requirements chapter, a chapter containing energy efficiency requirements and existing building provisions applicable to buildings within its scope.

This comprehensive energy conservation code establishes minimum regulations for energy-efficient buildings using prescriptive and performance-related provisions. It is founded on broad-based principles that make possible the use of new materials and new energy-efficient designs. This 2015 edition is fully compatible with all of the *International Codes®* (I-Codes®) published by the International Code Council (ICC)®, including: the *International Building Code®, International Existing Building Code®, International Fire Code®, International Fuel Gas Code®, International Green Construction Code®, International Mechanical Code®,* ICC *Performance Code®, International Plumbing Code®, International Private Sewage Disposal Code®, International Property Maintenance Code®, International Residential Code®, International Swimming Pool and Spa Code™, International Wildland-Urban Interface Code®* and *International Zoning Code®*.

The *International Energy Conservation Code* provisions provide many benefits, among which is the model code development process that offers an international forum for energy professionals to discuss performance and prescriptive code requirements. This forum provides an excellent arena to debate proposed revisions. This model code also encourages international consistency in the application of provisions.

Development

The first edition of the *International Energy Conservation Code* (1998) was based on the 1995 edition of the *Model Energy Code* promulgated by the Council of American Building Officials (CABO) and included changes approved through the CABO Code Development Procedures through 1997. CABO assigned all rights and responsibilities to the International Code Council and its three statutory members at that time, including Building Officials and Code Administrators International, Inc. (BOCA), International Conference of Building Officials (ICBO) and Southern Building Code Congress International (SBCCI). This 2015 edition presents the code as originally issued, with changes reflected in the 2000 through 2012 editions and with changes approved through the ICC Code Development Process through 2014. A new edition such as this is promulgated every 3 years.

This code is founded on principles intended to establish provisions consistent with the scope of an energy conservation code that adequately conserves energy; provisions that do not unnecessarily increase construction costs; provisions that do not restrict the use of new materials, products or methods of construction; and provisions that do not give preferential treatment to particular types or classes of materials, products or methods of construction.

Adoption

The International Code Council maintains a copyright in all of its codes and standards. Maintaining copyright allows the ICC to fund its mission through sales of books, in both print and electronic formats. The *International Energy Conservation Code* is designed for adoption and use by jurisdictions that recognize and acknowledge the ICC's copyright in the code, and further acknowledge the substantial shared value of the public/private partnership for code development between jurisdictions and the ICC.

The ICC also recognizes the need for jurisdictions to make laws available to the public. All ICC codes and ICC standards, along with the laws of many jurisdictions, are available for free in a non-downloadable form on the ICC's website. Jurisdictions should contact the ICC at adoptions@iccsafe.org to learn how to adopt and distribute laws based on the *International Energy Conservation Code* in a manner that provides necessary access, while maintaining the ICC's copyright.

Maintenance

The *International Energy Conservation Code* is kept up to date through the review of proposed changes submitted by code enforcing officials, industry representatives, design professionals and other interested parties. Proposed changes are carefully considered through an open code development process in which all interested and affected parties may participate.

The contents of this work are subject to change through both the code development cycles and the governmental body that enacts the code into law. For more information regarding the code development process, contact the Codes and Standards Development Department of the International Code Council.

While the development procedure of the *International Energy Conservation Code* assures the highest degree of care, the ICC, its members and those participating in the development of this code do not accept any liability resulting from compliance or noncompliance with the provisions because the ICC does not have the power or authority to police or enforce compliance with the contents of this code. Only the governmental body that enacts the code into law has such authority.

Code Development Committee Responsibilities
(Letter Designations in Front of Section Numbers)

In each code development cycle, proposed changes to the code are considered at the Committee Action Hearings by the applicable International Code Development Committee. The IECC—Commercial Provisions (sections designated with a "C" prior to the section number) are primarily maintained by the Commercial Energy Code Development Committee. The IECC—Residential Provisions (sections designated with an "R" prior to the section number) are maintained by the Residential Energy Code Development Committee. This is designated in the chapter headings by a [CE] and [RE], respectively.

Maintenance responsibilities for the IECC are designated as follows:

[CE] = Commercial Energy Code Development Committee

[RE] = Residential Energy Code Development Committee

Providing for Michigan's Safety in the Built Environment

2015

WITHDRAWN

MICHIGAN ENERGY CODE

Incorporating the 2015 edition of the
International Energy Conservation
Code®

Michigan Department of Licensing and Regulatory Affairs
Bureau of Construction Codes

ICC
INTERNATIONAL
CODE COUNCIL®

2015 Michigan Energy Code

First Printing: June 2017

ISBN: 978-1-60983-704-4

PRINTED IN THE U.S.A.

For the development of the 2018 edition of the I-Codes, there will be three groups of code development committees and they will meet in separate years. Note that these are tentative groupings.

Group A Codes (Heard in 2015, Code Change Proposals Deadline: January 12, 2015)	Group B Codes (Heard in 2016, Code Change Proposals Deadline: January 11, 2016)	Group C Codes (Heard in 2017, Code Change Proposals Deadline: January 11, 2017)
International Building Code –Fire Safety (Chapters 7, 8, 9, 14, 26) –Means of Egress (Chapters 10, 11, Appendix E) –General (Chapters 2-6, 12, 27-33, Appendices A, B, C, D, K)	Administrative Provisions (Chapter 1 of all codes except IRC and IECC, administrative updates to currently referenced standards, and designated definitions)	International Green Construction Code
International Fuel Gas Code	International Building Code –Structural (Chapters 15-25, Appendices F, G, H, I, J, L, M)	
International Existing Building Code	**International Energy Conservation Code**	
International Mechanical Code	International Fire Code	
International Plumbing Code	International Residential Code –IRC-Building (Chapters 1-10, Appendices E, F, H, J, K, L, M, O, R, S, T, U)	
International Private Sewage Disposal Code	International Wildland-Urban Interface Code	
International Property Maintenance Code		
International Residential Code –IRC-Mechanical (Chapters 12-24) –IRC-Plumbing (Chapters 25-33, Appendices G, I, N, P)		
International Swimming Pool and Spa Code		
International Zoning Code		

Note: Proposed changes to the ICC *Performance Code* will be heard by the code development committee noted in brackets [ ] in the text of the code.

Marginal Markings

Solid vertical lines in the margins within the body of the code indicate a technical change from the requirements of the 2012 edition. Deletion indicators in the form of an arrow (➡) are provided in the margin where an entire section, paragraph, exception or table has been deleted or an item in a list of items or a table has been deleted. Double vertical lines in the margin denote amendments and additions promulgated by the State of Michigan Department of Labor and Economic Growth, modifying the 2012 *International Energy Conservation Code*. An asterisk in the margin identifies sections of the 2015 *International Energy Conservation Code* not adopted by the State of Michigan.

A single bullet [•] placed in the margin indicates that text or a table has been relocated within the code. A double bullet [••] placed in the margin indicates that the text or table immediately following it has been relocated there from elsewhere in the code. The following table indicates such relocations in the 2015 *International Energy Conservation Code*.

2015 LOCATION	2012 LOCATION
C501	C101.4.1
C501.6	C101.4.2
C502 through C504	C101.4.3
C505	C101.4.4
C503.2	C101.4.5
C402.1.1	C101.5.2
C402.3	C402.2.1.1

2015 LOCATION	2012 LOCATION
R501	R101.4.1
R501.6	R101.4.2
R502 through R504	R101.4.3
R505	R101.4.4
R503.2	R101.4.5
R402.1	R101.5.2
R503.1.1.1	R402.3.6

Italicized Terms

Selected terms set forth in Chapter 2, Definitions, are italicized where they appear in code text. Such terms are not italicized where the definition set forth in Chapter 2 does not impart the intended meaning in the use of the term. The terms selected have definitions that the user should read carefully to facilitate better understanding of the code.

EFFECTIVE USE OF THE INTERNATIONAL ENERGY CONSERVATION CODE

The *International Energy Conservation Code* (IECC) is a model code that regulates minimum energy conservation requirements for new buildings. The IECC addresses energy conservation requirements for all aspects of energy uses in both commercial and residential construction, including heating and ventilating, lighting, water heating, and power usage for appliances and building systems.

The IECC is a design document. For example, before one constructs a building, the designer must determine the minimum insulation *R*-values and fenestration *U*-factors for the building exterior envelope. Depending on whether the building is for residential use or for commercial use, the IECC sets forth minimum requirements for exterior envelope insulation, window and door *U*-factors and SHGC ratings, duct insulation, lighting and power efficiency, and water distribution insulation.

Arrangement and Format of the 2015 IECC

The IECC contains two separate sets of provisions—one for commercial buildings and one for residential buildings. Each set of provisions is applied separately to buildings within their scope. The IECC—Commercial Provisions apply to all buildings except for residential buildings three stories or less in height. The IECC—Residential Provisions apply to detached one- and two-family dwellings and multiple single-family dwellings as well as Group R-2, R-3 and R-4 buildings three stories or less in height. These scopes are based on the definitions of "Commercial building" and "Residential building," respectively, in Chapter 2 of each set of provisions. Note that the IECC—Commercial Provisions therefore contain provisions for residential buildings four stories or greater in height. Each set of provisions is divided into five different parts:

Chapters	Subjects
1-2	Administration and definitions
3	Climate zones and general materials requirements
4	Energy efficiency requirements
5	Existing buildings
6	Referenced standards

The following is a chapter-by-chapter synopsis of the scope and intent of the provisions of the *International Energy Conservation Code* and applies to both the commercial and residential energy provisions:

Chapter 1 Scope and Administration. This chapter contains provisions for the application, enforcement and administration of subsequent requirements of the code. In addition to establishing the scope of the code, Chapter 1 identifies which buildings and structures come under its purview. Chapter 1 is largely concerned with maintaining "due process of law" in enforcing the energy conservation criteria contained in the body of this code. Only through careful observation of the administrative provisions can the code official reasonably expect to demonstrate that "equal protection under the law" has been provided.

Chapter 2 Definitions. Chapter 2 is the repository of the definitions of terms used in the body of the code. Codes are technical documents and every word, term and punctuation mark can impact the meaning of the code text and the intended results. The code often uses terms that have a unique meaning in the code and the code meaning can differ substantially from the ordinarily understood meaning of the term as used outside of the code.

The terms defined in Chapter 2 are deemed to be of prime importance in establishing the meaning and intent of the code text. The user of the code should be familiar with and consult this chapter because the definitions are essential to the correct interpretation of the code and the user may not be aware that a term is defined.

Additional definitions regarding climate zones are found in Tables 301.3(1) and (2). These are not listed in Chapter 2.

Where understanding of a term's definition is especially key to or necessary for understanding of a particular code provision, the term is shown in *italics* wherever it appears in the code. This is true only for those terms that have a meaning that is unique to the code. In other words, the generally understood meaning of a term or phrase might not be sufficient or consistent with the meaning prescribed by the code; therefore, it is essential that the code-defined meaning be known.

Guidance regarding tense, gender and plurality of defined terms as well as guidance regarding terms not defined in this code is provided.

Chapter 3 General Requirements. Chapter 3 specifies the climate zones that will serve to establish the exterior design conditions. In addition, Chapter 3 provides interior design conditions that are used as a basis for assumptions in heating and cooling load calculations, and provides basic material requirements for insulation materials and fenestration materials.

Climate has a major impact on the energy use of most buildings. The code establishes many requirements such as wall and roof insulation *R*-values, window and door thermal transmittance requirement (*U*-factors) as well as provisions that affect the mechanical systems based upon the climate where the building is located. This chapter contains information that will be used to properly assign the building location into the correct climate zone and is used as the basis for establishing requirements or elimination of requirements.

Chapter 4 Energy Efficiency. Chapter 4 of each set of provisions contains the technical requirements for energy efficiency.

Commercial Energy Efficiency. Chapter 4 of the IECC—Commercial Provisions contains the energy-efficiency-related requirements for the design and construction of most types of commercial buildings and residential buildings greater than three stories in height above grade. Residential buildings, townhouses and garden apartments three stories or less in height are covered in the IECC—Residential Provisions. This chapter defines requirements for the portions of the building and building systems that impact energy use in new commercial construction and new residential construction greater than three stories in height, and promotes the effective use of energy. The provisions within the chapter promote energy efficiency in the building envelope, the heating and cooling system and the service water heating system of the building.

Residential Energy Efficiency. Chapter 4 of the IECC—Residential Provisions contains the energy-efficiency-related requirements for the design and construction of residential buildings regulated under this code. It should be noted that the definition of a *residential building* in this code is unique for this code. In this code, a *residential building* is a detached one- and two-family dwelling and multiple single-family dwellings as well as R-2, R-3 or R-4 buildings three stories or less in height. All other buildings, including residential buildings greater than three stories in height, are regulated by the energy conservation requirements in the IECC—Commercial Provisions. The applicable portions of a residential building must comply with the provisions within this chapter for energy efficiency. This chapter defines requirements for the portions of the building and building systems that impact energy use in new residential construction and promotes the effective use of energy. The provisions within the chapter promote energy efficiency in the building envelope, the heating and cooling system and the service water heating system of the building.

Chapter 5 Existing Buildings. Chapter 5 of each set of provisions contains the technical energy efficiency requirements for existing buildings. Chapter 5 provisions address the maintenance of buildings in compliance with the code as well as how additions, alterations, repairs and changes of occupancy need to be addressed from the standpoint of energy efficiency. Specific provisions are provided for historic buildings.

Chapter 6 Referenced Standards. The code contains numerous references to standards that are used to regulate materials and methods of construction. Chapter 6 contains a comprehensive list of all standards that are referenced in the code. The standards are part of the code to the extent of the reference to the standard. Compliance with the referenced standard is necessary for compliance with this code. By providing specifically adopted standards, the construction and installation requirements necessary for compliance with the code can be readily determined. The basis for code compliance is, therefore, established and available on an equal basis to the code official, contractor, designer and owner.

Chapter 6 is organized in a manner that makes it easy to locate specific standards. It lists all of the referenced standards, alphabetically, by acronym of the promulgating agency of the standard. Each agency's standards are then listed in either alphabetical or numeric order based upon the standard identification. The list also contains the title of the standard; the edition (date) of the standard referenced; any addenda included as part of the ICC adoption; and the section or sections of this code that reference the standard.

Abbreviations and Notations

The following is a list of common abbreviations and units of measurement used in this code. Some of the abbreviations are for terms defined in Chapter 2. Others are terms used in various tables and text of the code.

AFUE	Annual fuel utilization efficiency
bhp	Brake horsepower (fans)
Btu	British thermal unit
Btu/h-ft^2	Btu per hour per square foot
C-factor	See Chapter 2—Definitions
CDD	Cooling degree days
cfm	Cubic feet per minute
cfm/ft^2	Cubic feet per minute per square foot
ci	Continuous insulation
COP	Coefficient of performance
DCV	Demand control ventilation
°C	Degrees Celsius
°F	Degrees Fahrenheit
DWHR	Drain water heat recovery
DX	Direct expansion
E_c	Combustion efficiency
E_v	Ventilation efficiency
E_t	Thermal efficiency
EER	Energy efficiency ratio
EF	Energy factor
ERI	Energy Rating index
F-factor	See Chapter 2—Definitions

FDD	Fault detection and diagnostics
FEG	Fan efficiency grade
FL	Full load
ft^2	Square foot
gpm	Gallons per minute
HDD	Heating degree days
hp	Horsepower
HSPF	Heating seasonal performance factor
HVAC	Heating, ventilating and air conditioning
IEER	Integrated energy efficiency ratio
IPLV	Integrated Part Load Value
Kg/m^2	Kilograms per square meter
kW	Kilowatt
LPD	Light power density (lighting power allowance)
L/s	Liters per second
Ls	Liner system
m^2	square meters
MERV	Minimum efficiency reporting value
NAECA	National Appliance Energy Conservation Act
NPLV	Nonstandard Part Load Value
Pa	Pascal
PF	Projection factor
pcf	Pounds per cubic foot
psf	Pounds per square foot
PTAC	Packaged terminal air conditioner
PTHP	Packaged terminal heat pump
R-value	See Chapter 2—Definitions
SCOP	Sensible coefficient of performance
SEER	Seasonal energy efficiency ratio
SHGC	Solar Heat Gain Coefficient
SPVAC	Single packaged vertical air conditioner
SPVHP	Single packaged vertical heat pump
SRI	Solar reflectance index
SWHF	Service water heat recovery factor
U-factor	See Chapter 2—Definitions
VAV	Variable air volume
VRF	Variable refrigerant flow
VT	Visible transmittance
W	Watts
w.c.	Water column
w.g.	Water gauge

TABLE OF CONTENTS

IECC—COMMERCIAL PROVISIONS

TABLE OF CONTENTS

CHAPTER 1 [CE]

SCOPE AND ADMINISTRATION

PART 1—SCOPE AND APPLICATION

SECTION C101
SCOPE AND GENERAL REQUIREMENTS

C101.1 Title. This code shall be known and cited as the "Michigan Energy Code." It is referred to herein as "this code."

R 408.31088a

C101.2 Scope. This code applies to *commercial buildings* and the buildings' sites and associated systems and equipment.

C101.3 Intent. This code shall regulate the design and construction of buildings for the use and conservation of energy over the life of each building. This code is intended to provide flexibility to permit the use of innovative approaches and techniques to achieve this objective. This code is not intended to abridge safety, health or environmental requirements contained in other applicable codes or ordinances.

C101.4 Applicability. Where, in any specific case, different sections of this code specify different materials, methods of construction or other requirements, the most restrictive shall govern. Where there is a conflict between a general requirement and a specific requirement, the specific requirement shall govern.

> **C101.4.1 Mixed occupancy.** Where a building includes both *residential* and *commercial* occupancies, each occupancy shall be separately considered and meet the applicable provisions of IECC—Commercial Provisions or IECC—Residential Provisions.

C101.5 Compliance. *Residential buildings* shall meet the provisions of IECC—Residential Provisions. *Commercial buildings* shall meet the provisions of IECC—Commercial Provisions.

> **C101.5.1 Compliance materials.** The *code official* shall be permitted to approve specific computer software, worksheets, compliance manuals and other similar materials that meet the intent of this code.

SECTION C102
ALTERNATE MATERIALS—METHOD OF CONSTRUCTION, DESIGN OR INSULATING SYSTEMS

C102.1 General. This code is not intended to prevent the use of any material, method of construction, design or insulating system not specifically prescribed herein, provided that such construction, design or insulating system has been *approved* by the *code official* as meeting the intent of this code.

> **C102.1.1 Above code programs.** The state construction code commission may evaluate and approve a national, state, or local energy efficiency program to exceed the energy efficiency required by this code. Buildings approved in writing by an energy efficiency program, such as ICC 700-2012 "silver" or energy star version 3 (rev. 07), shall be considered in compliance with this code. The requirements identified as "mandatory" in chapter 4 shall be met.

R 408.31092

PART 2—ADMINISTRATION AND ENFORCEMENT

SECTION C103
CONSTRUCTION DOCUMENTS

C103.1 Submittal documents. Construction documents, special inspection and structural programs, and other data shall meet both of the following requirements:

(1) Be submitted in 1 or more sets with each application for a permit.

(2) Be prepared by, or under the direct supervision of, a registered design professional when required by the Occupational Code, 1980 PA 299, MCL 339.101 to 339.2919.

Where special conditions exist, the building official may require additional construction documents to be prepared by a registered design professional.

R 408.31092

C103.2 Information on construction documents. Construction documents shall be drawn to scale upon suitable material. Electronic media documents are permitted to be submitted where *approved* by the *code official*. Construction documents shall be of sufficient clarity to indicate the location, nature and extent of the work proposed, and show in sufficient detail pertinent data and features of the building, systems and equipment as herein governed. Details shall include, but are not limited to, the following as applicable:

1. Insulation materials and their *R*-values.

2. Fenestration *U*-factors and solar heat gain coefficients (SHGCs).

3. Area-weighted *U*-factor and solar heat gain coefficient (SHGC) calculations.

4. Mechanical system design criteria.

5. Mechanical and service water heating system and equipment types, sizes and efficiencies.

6. Economizer description.

7. Equipment and system controls.

8. Fan motor horsepower (hp) and controls.

9. Duct sealing, duct and pipe insulation and location.

10. Lighting fixture schedule with wattage and control narrative.

11. Location of *daylight* zones on floor plans.

12. Air sealing details.

C103.2.1 Building thermal envelope depiction. The *building's thermal envelope* shall be represented on the construction drawings.

C103.3 Examination of documents. The *code official* shall examine or cause to be examined the accompanying construction documents and shall ascertain whether the construction indicated and described is in accordance with the requirements of this code and other pertinent laws or ordinances. The *code official* is authorized to utilize a registered design professional, or other *approved* entity not affiliated with the building design or construction, in conducting the review of the plans and specifications for compliance with the code.

C103.3.1 Approval of construction documents. When the *code official* issues a permit where construction documents are required, the construction documents shall be endorsed in writing and stamped "Reviewed for Code Compliance." Such *approved* construction documents shall not be changed, modified or altered without authorization from the *code official*. Work shall be done in accordance with the *approved* construction documents.

One set of construction documents so reviewed shall be retained by the *code official*. The other set shall be returned to the applicant, kept at the site of work and shall be open to inspection by the *code official* or a duly authorized representative.

C103.3.2 Previous approvals. This code shall not require changes in the construction documents, construction or designated occupancy of a structure for which a lawful permit has been heretofore issued or otherwise lawfully authorized, and the construction of which has been pursued in good faith within 180 days after the effective date of this code and has not been abandoned.

C103.3.3 Phased approval. The *code official* shall have the authority to issue a permit for the construction of part of an energy conservation system before the construction documents for the entire system have been submitted or *approved*, provided adequate information and detailed statements have been filed complying with all pertinent requirements of this code. The holders of such permit shall proceed at their own risk without assurance that the permit for the entire energy conservation system will be granted.

C103.4 Amended construction documents. Changes made during construction that are not in compliance with the *approved* construction documents shall be resubmitted for approval as an amended set of construction documents.

C103.5 Retention of construction documents. One set of *approved* construction documents shall be retained by the *code official* for a period of not less than 180 days from date of completion of the permitted work, or as required by state or local laws.

SECTION C104
INSPECTIONS

C104.1 General. Construction or work for which a permit is required shall be subject to inspection by the *code official* or his or her designated agent, and such construction or work shall remain accessible and exposed for inspection purposes until *approved*. It shall be the duty of the permit applicant to cause the work to remain accessible and exposed for inspection purposes. Neither the *code official* nor the jurisdiction shall be liable for expense entailed in the removal or replacement of any material, product, system or building component required to allow inspection to validate compliance with this code.

C104.2 Required energy efficiency inspections. The code official or his or her designated agent, upon notification, shall make the inspections set forth in Sections C104.2.1 through C104.2.6.

R 408.31092a

C104.2.1 Footing and foundation inspection. Inspections associated with footings and foundations shall verify compliance with the code as to *R*-value, location, thickness, depth of burial and protection of insulation as required by the code and *approved* plans and specifications.

C104.2.2 Framing and rough-in inspection. Inspections at framing and rough-in shall be made before application of interior finish and shall verify compliance with the code as to types of insulation and corresponding *R*-values and their correct location and proper installation; fenestration properties (*U*-factor, SHGC and VT) and proper installation; and air leakage controls as required by the code and approved plans and specifications.

C104.2.3 Plumbing rough-in inspection. Inspections at plumbing rough-in shall verify compliance as required by the code and *approved* plans and specifications as to types of insulation and corresponding *R*-values and protection; required controls; and required heat traps.

C104.2.4 Mechanical rough-in inspection. Inspections at mechanical rough-in shall verify compliance as required by the code and *approved* plans and specifications as to installed HVAC equipment type and size; required controls, system insulation and corresponding *R*-value; system and damper air leakage; and required energy recovery and economizers.

C104.2.5 Electrical rough-in inspection. Inspections at electrical rough-in shall verify compliance as required by the code and *approved* plans and specifications as to installed lighting systems, components and controls; and installation of an electric meter for each dwelling unit.

C104.2.6 Final inspection. The building shall have a final inspection and shall not be occupied until *approved*. The final inspection shall include verification of the installation and proper operation of all required building controls, and documentation verifying activities associated with required *building commissioning* have been conducted and findings of noncompliance corrected. Buildings, or portions thereof, shall not be considered for a final inspection until the *code official* has received a letter of transmittal from the building owner acknowledging that the building owner has received the Preliminary Commissioning Report as required in Section C408.2.4.

C104.3 Reinspection. A building shall be reinspected when determined necessary by the *code official*.

C104.4 Approved inspection agencies. The *code official* is authorized to accept reports of third-party inspection agencies not affiliated with the building design or construction, provided such agencies are *approved* as to qualifications and reliability relevant to the building components and systems they are inspecting.

C104.5 Inspection requests. It shall be the duty of the holder of the permit or their duly authorized agent to notify the *code official* when work is ready for inspection. It shall be the duty of the permit holder to provide access to and means for inspections of such work that are required by this code.

C104.6 Reinspection and testing. Where any work or installation does not pass an initial test or inspection, the necessary corrections shall be made to achieve compliance with this code. The work or installation shall then be resubmitted to the *code official* for inspection and testing.

C104.7 Approval. After the prescribed tests and inspections indicate that the work complies in all respects with this code, a notice of approval shall be issued by the *code official*.

C104.7.1 Revocation. The *code official* is authorized to, in writing, suspend or revoke a notice of approval issued under the provisions of this code wherever the certificate is issued in error, or on the basis of incorrect information supplied, or where it is determined that the *building* or structure, premise, or portion thereof is in violation of any ordinance or regulation or any of the provisions of this code.

C104.8 Administrative requirements. Administrative requirements relating to permits, enforcement, interpretations, and appeals shall be pursuant to the Stille-DeRossett-Hale Single State Construction Code Act, 1972 PA 230, MCL 125.1501 to 125.1531.

R 408.31090

SECTION C105
VALIDITY

C105.1 General. If a portion of this code is held to be illegal or void, such a decision shall not affect the validity of the remainder of this code.

SECTION C106
REFERENCED STANDARDS

C106.1 Referenced codes and standards. The codes and standards referenced in this code shall be those listed in Chapter 6, and such codes and standards shall be considered as part of the requirements of this code to the prescribed

extent of each such reference and as further regulated in Sections C106.1.1 and C106.1.2.

C106.1.1 Conflicts. Where conflicts occur between provisions of this code and referenced codes and standards, the provisions of this code shall apply.

C106.1.2 Provisions in referenced codes and standards. Where the extent of the reference to a referenced code or standard includes subject matter that is within the scope of this code, the provisions of this code, as applicable, shall take precedence over the provisions in the referenced code or standard.

C106.2 Application of references. References to chapter or section numbers, or to provisions not specifically identified by number, shall be construed to refer to such chapter, section or provision of this code.

C106.3 Other laws. The provisions of this code shall not be deemed to nullify any provisions of local, state or federal law.

SECTION C107
FEES

C107.1 Payment of fees. The fees prescribed by the Stille-DeRossett-Hale Single State Construction Code Act, 1972 PA 230, MCL 125.1501 to 125.1531 shall be paid to the enforcing agency of the jurisdiction before a permit to begin work for new construction, alteration, removal, demolition, or other building operation may be issued. In addition, an amendment to a permit requiring an additional fee shall not be approved until the additional fee has been paid.

R 408.31093

SECTION C108
STOP WORK ORDER

C108.1 Stop work orders. Notice shall be in accordance with the Stille-DeRossett-Hale Single State Construction Code Act, 1972 PA 203, MCL 125.1501 to 125.1531. A person who is served with a stop work order, except for work that the person is directed to perform to remove a violation or unsafe condition, is subject to the penalty provisions prescribed by the act.

R 408.31094

SECTION C109
BOARD OF APPEALS

C109.1 Means of appeal.

(1) An interested person may appeal a decision of the enforcing agency to the board of appeals in accordance with the act.

(2) The decision of a local board of appeals may be appealed to the construction code commission in accordance with the act and time frames contained in the act.

R 408.31095

C109.2 Limitations on authority. An application for appeal shall be based on a claim that the true intent of this code or the rules legally adopted thereunder have been incorrectly interpreted, the provisions of this code do not fully apply or an equally good or better form of construction is proposed. The board shall not have authority to waive requirements of this code.

C109.3 Qualifications. The board of appeals shall consist of members who are qualified in accordance with the act.

R 408.31060c

CHAPTER 2 [CE]
DEFINITIONS

SECTION C201
GENERAL

C201.1 Scope. Unless stated otherwise, the following words and terms in this code shall have the meanings indicated in this chapter.

C201.2 Interchangeability. Words used in the present tense include the future; words in the masculine gender include the feminine and neuter; the singular number includes the plural and the plural includes the singular.

C201.3 Terms defined in other codes. Terms that are not defined in this code but are defined in the *International Building Code, International Fire Code, International Fuel Gas Code, International Mechanical Code, International Plumbing Code* or the *International Residential Code* shall have the meanings ascribed to them in those codes.

C201.4 Terms not defined. Terms not defined by this chapter shall have ordinarily accepted meanings such as the context implies.

SECTION C202
GENERAL DEFINITIONS

ABOVE-GRADE WALL. See "Wall, above-grade."

ACCESSIBLE. Admitting close approach as a result of not being guarded by locked doors, elevation or other effective means (see "Readily *accessible*").

ADDITION. An extension or increase in the *conditioned space* floor area or height of a building or structure.

AIR BARRIER. Materials assembled and joined together to provide a barrier to air leakage through the building envelope. An air barrier may be a single material or a combination of materials.

AIR CURTAIN. A device, installed at the building entrance, that generates and discharges a laminar air stream intended to prevent the infiltration of external, unconditioned air into the conditioned spaces, or the loss of interior, conditioned air to the outside.

ALTERATION. Any construction, retrofit or renovation to an existing structure other than repair or addition that requires a permit. Also, a change in a building, electrical, gas, mechanical or plumbing system that involves an extension, addition or change to the arrangement, type or purpose of the original installation that requires a permit.

APPROVED. Approval by the *code official* as a result of investigation and tests conducted by him or her, or by reason of accepted principles or tests by nationally recognized organizations.

APPROVED AGENCY. An established and recognized agency regularly engaged in conducting tests or furnishing inspection services, when such agency has been approved by the *code official*.

AUTOMATIC. Self-acting, operating by its own mechanism when actuated by some impersonal influence, as, for example, a change in current strength, pressure, temperature or mechanical configuration (see "Manual").

BELOW-GRADE WALL. See "Wall, below-grade."

BOILER, MODULATING. A boiler that is capable of more than a single firing rate in response to a varying temperature or heating load.

BOILER SYSTEM. One or more boilers, their piping and controls that work together to supply steam or hot water to heat output devices remote from the boiler.

BUBBLE POINT. The refrigerant liquid saturation temperature at a specified pressure.

BUILDING. "Building" as defined in the Stille-DeRossett-Hale Single State Construction Code Act, 1972 PA 230, MCL 125.1501 to 125.1531.

R 408.31088

BUILDING COMMISSIONING. A process that verifies and documents that the selected building systems have been designed, installed, and function according to the owner's project requirements and construction documents, and to minimum code requirements.

BUILDING ENTRANCE. Any door, set of doors, doorway, or other form of portal that is used to gain access to the building from the outside by the public.

BUILDING OFFICIAL. "Building official" as defined in the Stille-DeRossett-Hale Single State Construction Code Act, 1972 PA 230, MCL 125.1501 to 125.1531.

R 408.31088

BUILDING SITE. A contiguous area of land that is under the ownership or control of one entity.

BUILDING THERMAL ENVELOPE. The basement walls, exterior walls, floor, roof and any other building elements that enclose *conditioned space* or provide a boundary between *conditioned space* and exempt or unconditioned space.

***C*-FACTOR (THERMAL CONDUCTANCE).** The coefficient of heat transmission (surface to surface) through a building component or assembly, equal to the time rate of heat flow per unit area and the unit temperature difference between the warm side and cold side surfaces (Btu/h · ft^2 · °F) [W/(m^2 · K)].

CIRCULATING HOT WATER SYSTEM. A specifically designed water distribution system where one or more pumps are operated in the service hot water piping to circulate heated water from the water-heating equipment to the fixture supply and back to the water-heating equipment.

CLIMATE ZONE. A geographical region based on climatic criteria as specified in this code.

CODE OFFICIAL. The officer or other designated authority charged with the administration and enforcement of this code, or a duly authorized representative.

COEFFICENT OF PERFORMANCE (COP) – COOLING. The ratio of the rate of heat input, in consistent units, for a complete refrigerating system or some specific portion of that system under designated operating conditions.

COEFFICIENT OF PERFORMANCE (COP) – HEATING. The ratio of the rate of heat delivered to the rate of energy input, in consistent units, for a complete heat pump system, including the compressor and, if applicable, auxiliary heat, under designated operating conditions.

COMMERCIAL BUILDING. For this code, all buildings that are not included in the definition of "Residential building."

COMPUTER ROOM. A room whose primary function is to house equipment for the processing and storage of electronic data and that has a design electronic data equipment power density exceeding 20 watts per square foot of conditioned floor area.

CONDENSING UNIT. A factory-made assembly of refrigeration components designed to compress and liquefy a specific refrigerant. The unit consists of one or more refrigerant compressors, refrigerant condensers (air-cooled, evaporatively cooled, or water-cooled), condenser fans and motors (where used) and factory-supplied accessories.

CONDITIONED FLOOR AREA. The horizontal projection of the floors associated with the *conditioned space*.

CONDITIONED SPACE. An area, room or space that is enclosed within the building thermal envelope and is directly or indirectly heated or cooled. Spaces are indirectly heated or cooled where they communicate through openings with conditioned spaces, where they are separated from conditioned spaces by uninsulated walls, floors or ceilings, or where they contain uninsulated ducts, piping or other sources of heating or cooling.

CONTINUOUS AIR BARRIER. A combination of materials and assemblies that restrict or prevent the passage of air through the building thermal envelope.

CONTINUOUS INSULATION (ci). Insulating material that is continuous across all structural members without thermal bridges other than fasteners and service openings. It is installed on the interior or exterior or is integral to any opaque surface of the building envelope.

CRAWL SPACE WALL. The opaque portion of a wall that encloses a crawl space and is partially or totally below grade.

CURTAIN WALL. Fenestration products used to create an external nonload-bearing wall that is designed to separate the exterior and interior environments.

DAYLIGHT RESPONSIVE CONTROL. A device or system that provides automatic control of electric light levels based on the amount of daylight in a space.

DAYLIGHT ZONE. That portion of a building's interior floor area that is illuminated by natural light.

DEMAND CONTROL VENTILATION (DCV). A ventilation system capability that provides for the automatic reduction of outdoor air intake below design rates when the actual occupancy of spaces served by the system is less than design occupancy.

DEMAND RECIRCULATION WATER SYSTEM. A water distribution system where pumps prime the service hot water piping with heated water upon demand for hot water.

DUCT. A tube or conduit utilized for conveying air. The air passages of self-contained systems are not to be construed as air ducts.

DUCT SYSTEM. A continuous passageway for the transmission of air that, in addition to ducts, includes duct fittings, dampers, plenums, fans and accessory air-handling equipment and appliances.

[B] DWELLING UNIT. A single unit providing complete independent living facilities for one or more persons, including permanent provisions for living, sleeping, eating, cooking and sanitation.

DYNAMIC GLAZING. Any fenestration product that has the fully reversible ability to change its performance properties, including *U*-factor, solar heat gain coefficient (SHGC), or visible transmittance (VT).

ECONOMIZER, AIR. A duct and damper arrangement and automatic control system that allows a cooling system to supply outside air to reduce or eliminate the need for mechanical cooling during mild or cold weather.

ECONOMIZER, WATER. A system where the supply air of a cooling system is cooled indirectly with water that is itself cooled by heat or mass transfer to the environment without the use of mechanical cooling.

ENCLOSED SPACE. A volume surrounded by solid surfaces such as walls, floors, roofs, and openable devices such as doors and operable windows.

ENERGY ANALYSIS. A method for estimating the annual energy use of the *proposed design* and *standard reference design* based on estimates of energy use.

ENERGY COST. The total estimated annual cost for purchased energy for the building functions regulated by this code, including applicable demand charges.

[M] ENERGY RECOVERY VENTILATION SYSTEM. Systems that employ air-to-air heat exchangers to recover energy from exhaust air for the purpose of preheating, precooling, humidifying or dehumidifying outdoor ventilation air prior to supplying the air to a space, either directly or as part of an HVAC system.

ENERGY SIMULATION TOOL. An *approved* software program or calculation-based methodology that projects the annual energy use of a building.

ENTRANCE DOOR. Fenestration products used for ingress, egress and access in nonresidential buildings, including, but not limited to, exterior entrances that utilize latching hardware and automatic closers and contain over 50-percent glass specifically designed to withstand heavy use and possibly abuse.

EQUIPMENT ROOM. A space that contains either electrical equipment, mechanical equipment, machinery, water pumps or hydraulic pumps that are a function of the building's services.

EXTERIOR WALL. Walls including both above-grade walls and basement walls.

FAN BRAKE HORSEPOWER (BHP). The horsepower delivered to the fan's shaft. Brake horsepower does not include the mechanical drive losses (belts, gears, etc.).

FAN EFFICIENCY GRADE (FEG). A numerical rating identifying the fan's aerodynamic ability to convert shaft power, or impeller power in the case of a direct-driven fan, to air power.

FAN SYSTEM BHP. The sum of the fan brake horsepower of all fans that are required to operate at fan system design conditions to supply air from the heating or cooling source to the *conditioned spaces* and return it to the source or exhaust it to the outdoors.

FAN SYSTEM DESIGN CONDITIONS. Operating conditions that can be expected to occur during normal system operation that result in the highest supply fan airflow rate to conditioned spaces served by the system.

FAN SYSTEM MOTOR NAMEPLATE HP. The sum of the motor nameplate horsepower of all fans that are required to operate at design conditions to supply air from the heating or cooling source to the *conditioned spaces* and return it to the source or exhaust it to the outdoors.

FENESTRATION. Products classified as either vertical fenestration or skylights.

> **Skylight.** Glass or other transparent or translucent glazing material installed at a slope of less than 60 degrees (1.05 rad) from horizontal.

> **Vertical fenestration.** Windows (fixed or moveable), opaque doors, glazed doors, glazed block and combination opaque/glazed doors composed of glass or other transparent or translucent glazing materials and installed at a slope of at least 60 degrees (1.05 rad) from horizontal.

FENESTRATION PRODUCT, FIELD-FABRICATED. A fenestration product whose frame is made at the construction site of standard dimensional lumber or other materials that were not previously cut, or otherwise formed with the specific intention of being used to fabricate a fenestration product or exterior door. Field fabricated does not include site-built fenestration.

FENESTRATION PRODUCT, SITE-BUILT. A fenestration designed to be made up of field-glazed or field-assembled units using specific factory cut or otherwise factory-formed framing and glazing units. Examples of site-built fenestration include storefront systems, curtain walls, and atrium roof systems.

F-FACTOR. The perimeter heat loss factor for slab-on-grade floors (Btu/h · ft · °F) [W/(m · K)].

FLOOR AREA, NET. The actual occupied area not including unoccupied accessory areas such as corridors, stairways, toilet rooms, mechanical rooms and closets.

GENERAL LIGHTING. Lighting that provides a substantially uniform level of illumination throughout an area. General lighting shall not include decorative lighting or lighting that provides a dissimilar level of illumination to serve a specialized application or feature within such area.

GENERAL PURPOSE ELECTRIC MOTOR (SUBTYPE I). A motor that is designed in standard ratings with either of the following:

1. Standard operating characteristics and standard mechanical construction for use under usual service conditions, such as those specified in NEMA MG1, paragraph 14.02, "Usual Service Conditions," and without restriction to a particular application or type of application.

2. Standard operating characteristics or standard mechanical construction for use under unusual service conditions, such as those specified in NEMA MG1, paragraph 14.03, "Unusual Service Conditions," or for a particular type of application, and that can be used in most general purpose applications.

General purpose electric motors (Subtype I) are constructed in NEMA T-frame sizes or IEC metric equivalent, starting at 143T.

GENERAL PURPOSE ELECTRIC MOTOR (SUBTYPE II). A motor incorporating the design elements of a general purpose electric motor (Subtype I) that is configured as one of the following:

1. A U-frame motor.
2. A Design C motor.
3. A close-coupled pump motor.
4. A footless motor.
5. A vertical, solid-shaft, normal-thrust motor (as tested in a horizontal configuration).
6. An 8-pole motor (900 rpm).
7. A polyphase motor with voltage of not more than 600 volts (other than 230 or 460 volts).

GREENHOUSE. A structure or a thermally isolated area of a building that maintains a specialized sunlit environment exclusively used for, and essential to, the cultivation, protection or maintenance of plants.

HEAT TRAP. An arrangement of piping and fittings, such as elbows, or a commercially available heat trap that prevents thermosyphoning of hot water during standby periods.

HEATED SLAB. Slab-on-grade construction in which the heating elements, hydronic tubing, or hot air distribution system is in contact with, or placed within or under, the slab.

HIGH SPEED DOOR. A nonswinging door used primarily to facilitate vehicular access or material transportation, with a minimum opening rate of 32 inches (813 mm) per second, a minimum closing rate of 24 inches (610 mm) per second and that includes an automatic-closing device.

HISTORIC BUILDING. Any building or structure that is one or more of the following:

1. Listed, or certified as eligible for listing by the State Historic Preservation Officer or the Keeper of the

National Register of Historic Places, in the National Register of Historic Places.

2. Designated as historic under an applicable state or local law.

3. Certified as a contributing resource within a National Register-listed, state-designated or locally designated historic district.

HUMIDISTAT. A regulatory device, actuated by changes in humidity, used for automatic control of relative humidity.

INFILTRATION. The uncontrolled inward air leakage into a building caused by the pressure effects of wind or the effect of differences in the indoor and outdoor air density or both.

➡ **INTEGRATED PART LOAD VALUE (IPLV).** A single-number figure of merit based on part-load EER, COP or kW/ton expressing part-load efficiency for air-conditioning and heat pump equipment on the basis of weighted operation at various load capacities for equipment.

LABELED. Equipment, materials or products to which have been affixed a label, seal, symbol or other identifying mark of a nationally recognized testing laboratory, inspection agency or other organization concerned with product evaluation that maintains periodic inspection of the production of the above-labeled items and whose labeling indicates either that the equipment, material or product meets identified standards or has been tested and found suitable for a specified purpose.

LINER SYSTEM (Ls). A system that includes the following:

1. A continuous vapor barrier liner membrane that is installed below the purlins and that is uninterrupted by framing members.

2. An uncompressed, unfaced insulation resting on top of the liner membrane and located between the purlins.

For multilayer installations, the last rated *R-value* of insulation is for unfaced insulation draped over purlins and then compressed when the metal roof panels are attached.

LISTED. Equipment, materials, products or services included in a list published by an organization acceptable to the *code official* and concerned with evaluation of products or services that maintains periodic inspection of production of *listed* equipment or materials or periodic evaluation of services and whose listing states either that the equipment, material, product or service meets identified standards or has been tested and found suitable for a specified purpose.

LOW-SLOPED ROOF. A roof having a slope less than 2 units vertical in 12 units horizontal.

LOW-VOLTAGE DRY-TYPE DISTRIBUTION TRANSFORMER. A transformer that is air-cooled, does not use oil as a coolant, has an input voltage less than or equal to 600 volts and is rated for operation at a frequency of 60 hertz.

LOW-VOLTAGE LIGHTING. Lighting equipment powered through a transformer such as a cable conductor, a rail conductor and track lighting.

MANUAL. Capable of being operated by personal intervention (see "Automatic").

NAMEPLATE HORSEPOWER. The nominal motor horsepower rating stamped on the motor nameplate.

NONSTANDARD PART LOAD VALUE (NPLV). A single-number part-load efficiency figure of merit calculated and referenced to conditions other than IPLV conditions, for units that are not designed to operate at AHRI standard rating conditions.

OCCUPANT SENSOR CONTROL. An automatic control device or system that detects the presence or absence of people within an area and causes lighting, equipment or appliances to be regulated accordingly.

ON-SITE RENEWABLE ENERGY. Energy derived from solar radiation, wind, waves, tides, landfill gas, biomass or the internal heat of the earth. The energy system providing on-site renewable energy shall be located on the project site.

OPAQUE DOOR. A door that is not less than 50-percent opaque in surface area.

POWERED ROOF/WALL VENTILATORS. A fan consisting of a centrifugal or axial impeller with an integral driver in a weather-resistant housing and with a base designed to fit, usually by means of a curb, over a wall or roof opening.

PROPOSED DESIGN. A description of the proposed building used to estimate annual energy use for determining compliance based on total building performance.

RADIANT HEATING SYSTEM. A heating system that transfers heat to objects and surfaces within a conditioned space, primarily by infrared radiation.

READILY ACCESSIBLE. Capable of being reached quickly for operation, renewal or inspection without requiring those to whom ready access is requisite to climb over or remove obstacles or to resort to portable ladders or access equipment (see "*Accessible*").

REFRIGERANT DEW POINT. The refrigerant vapor saturation temperature at a specified pressure.

REFRIGERATED WAREHOUSE COOLER. An enclosed storage space capable of being refrigerated to temperatures above 32°F (0°C), that can be walked into and has a total chilled storage area of not less than 3,000 square feet (279 m²).

REFRIGERATED WAREHOUSE FREEZER. An enclosed storage space capable of being refrigerated to temperatures at or below 32°F (0°C), that can be walked into and has a total chilled storage area of not less than 3,000 square feet (279 m²).

REFRIGERATION SYSTEM, LOW TEMPERATURE. Systems for maintaining food product in a frozen state in refrigeration applications.

REFRIGERATION SYSTEM, MEDIUM TEMPERATURE. Systems for maintaining food product above freezing in refrigeration applications.

REGISTERED DESIGN PROFESSIONAL. An individual who is registered or licensed to practice their respective design profession as defined by the statutory requirements of the professional registration laws of the state or jurisdiction in which the project is to be constructed.

REPAIR. The reconstruction or renewal of any part of an existing building for the purpose of its maintenance or to correct damage.

REROOFING. The process of recovering or replacing an existing roof covering. See "Roof recover" and "Roof replacement."

RESIDENTIAL BUILDING. For this code, includes detached one- and two-family dwellings and multiple single-family dwellings (townhouses) as well as Group R-2, R-3 and R-4 buildings three stories or less in height above grade plane.

ROOF ASSEMBLY. A system designed to provide weather protection and resistance to design loads. The system consists of a roof covering and roof deck or a single component serving as both the roof covering and the roof deck. A roof assembly includes the roof covering, underlayment, roof deck, insulation, vapor retarder and interior finish.

ROOF RECOVER. The process of installing an additional roof covering over an existing roof covering without removing the existing roof covering.

ROOF REPAIR. Reconstruction or renewal of any part of an existing roof for the purpose of its maintenance.

ROOF REPLACMENT. The process of removing the existing roof covering, repairing any damaged substrate and installing a new roof covering.

ROOFTOP MONITOR. A raised section of a roof containing vertical fenestration along one or more sides.

R-**VALUE (THERMAL RESISTANCE).** The inverse of the time rate of heat flow through a body from one of its bounding surfaces to the other surface for a unit temperature difference between the two surfaces, under steady state conditions, per unit area ($h \cdot ft^2 \cdot °F/Btu$) [($m^2 \cdot K$)/W].

SATURATED CONDENSING TEMPERATURE. The saturation temperature corresponding to the measured refrigerant pressure at the condenser inlet for single component and azeotropic refrigerants, and the arithmetic average of the dew point and *bubble point* temperatures corresponding to the refrigerant pressure at the condenser entrance for zeotropic refrigerants.

SCREW LAMP HOLDERS. A lamp base that requires a screw-in-type lamp, such as a compact-fluorescent, incandescent or tungsten-halogen bulb.

SERVICE WATER HEATING. Supply of hot water for purposes other than comfort heating.

[B] SLEEPING UNIT. A room or space in which people sleep, which can also include permanent provisions for living, eating, and either sanitation or kitchen facilities but not both. Such rooms and spaces that are also part of a dwelling unit are not *sleeping units*.

SMALL ELECTRIC MOTOR. A general purpose, alternating current, single speed induction motor.

SOLAR HEAT GAIN COEFFICIENT (SHGC). The ratio of the solar heat gain entering the space through the fenestration assembly to the incident solar radiation. Solar heat gain includes directly transmitted solar heat and absorbed solar radiation which is then reradiated, conducted or convected into the space.

STANDARD REFERENCE DESIGN. A version of the *proposed design* that meets the minimum requirements of this code and is used to determine the maximum annual energy use requirement for compliance based on total building performance.

STOREFRONT. A nonresidential system of doors and windows mulled as a composite fenestration structure that has been designed to resist heavy use. *Storefront* systems include, but are not limited to, exterior fenestration systems that span from the floor level or above to the ceiling of the same story on commercial buildings, with or without mulled windows and doors.

THERMOSTAT. An automatic control device used to maintain temperature at a fixed or adjustable set point.

TIME SWITCH CONTROL. An automatic control device or system that controls lighting or other loads, including switching off, based on time schedules.

U-**FACTOR (THERMAL TRANSMITTANCE).** The coefficient of heat transmission (air to air) through a building component or assembly, equal to the time rate of heat flow per unit area and unit temperature difference between the warm side and cold side air films ($Btu/h \cdot ft^2 \cdot °F$) [$W/(m^2 \cdot K)$].

VARIABLE REFRIGERANT FLOW SYSTEM. An engineered direct-expansion (DX) refrigerant system that incorporates a common condensing unit, at least one variable-capacity compressor, a distributed refrigerant piping network to multiple indoor fan heating and cooling units each capable of individual zone temperature control, through integral zone temperature control devices and a common communications network. Variable refrigerant flow utilizes three or more steps of control on common interconnecting piping.

[M] VENTILATION. The natural or mechanical process of supplying conditioned or unconditioned air to, or removing such air from, any space.

[M] VENTILATION AIR. That portion of supply air that comes from outside (outdoors) plus any recirculated air that has been treated to maintain the desired quality of air within a designated space.

VISIBLE TRANSMITTANCE [VT]. The ratio of visible light entering the space through the fenestration product assembly to the incident visible light. Visible transmittance includes the effects of glazing material and frame and is expressed as a number between 0 and 1.

WALK-IN COOLER. An enclosed storage space capable of being refrigerated to temperatures above 32°F (0°C) and less than 55°F (12.8°C) that can be walked into, has a ceiling height of not less than 7 feet (2134 mm) and has a total chilled storage area of less than 3,000 square feet (279 m^2).

WALK-IN FREEZER. An enclosed storage space capable of being refrigerated to temperatures at or below 32°F (0°C) that can be walked into, has a ceiling height of not less than 7 feet (2134 mm) and has a total chilled storage area of less than 3,000 square feet (279 m^2).

WALL, ABOVE-GRADE. A wall associated with the *building thermal envelope* that is more than 15 percent above grade and is on the exterior of the building or any wall that is associated with the *building thermal envelope* that is not on the exterior of the building.

WALL, BELOW-GRADE. A wall associated with the basement or first story of the building that is part of the *building thermal envelope*, is not less than 85 percent below grade and is on the exterior of the building.

WATER HEATER. Any heating appliance or equipment that heats potable water and supplies such water to the potable hot water distribution system.

ZONE. A space or group of spaces within a building with heating or cooling requirements that are sufficiently similar so that desired conditions can be maintained throughout using a single controlling device.

GENERAL REQUIREMENTS

SECTION C301
CLIMATE ZONES

C301.1 General. Climate zones from Figures C301.1 and C301.1a, or Table C301.1 shall be used to determine the applicable requirements of this code.

R 408.31096

C301.4 Tropical climate zone. The tropical *climate zone* shall be defined as:

1. Hawaii, Puerto Rico, Guam, American Samoa, U.S. Virgin Islands, Commonwealth of Northern Mariana Islands; and

2. Islands in the area between the Tropic of Cancer and the Tropic of Capricorn.

TABLE C301.1
CLIMATE ZONES BY COUNTY

ZONES		
5A	**6A**	**7**
Allegan	Alcona	Baraga
Barry	Alger	Chippewa
Bay	Alpena	Gogebic
Berrien	Antrim	Houghton
Branch	Arenac	Iron
Calhoun	Benzie	Keweenaw
Cass	Charlevoix	Luce
Clinton	Cheboygan	Mackinac
Eaton	Clare	Ontonagon
Genesee	Crawford	Schoolcraft
Gratiot	Delta	
Hillsdale	Dickinson	
Ingham	Emmet	
Ionia	Gladwin	
Jackson	Grand Traverse	
Kalamazoo	Huron	
Kent	Iosco	
Lapeer	Isabella	
Lenawee	Kalkaska	
Livingston	Lake	
Macomb	Leelanau	
Midland	Manistee	
Monroe	Marquette	
Montcalm	Mason	
Muskegon	Mecosta	
Oakland	Menominee	
Ottawa	Missaukee	
Saginaw	Montmorency	
Shiawassee	Newaygo	
St. Clair	Oceana	
St. Joseph	Ogemaw	
Tuscola	Osceola	
Van Buren	Oscoda	
Washtenaw	Otsego	
Wayne	Presque Isle	
	Roscommon	
	Sanilac	
	Wexford	

Key: A – Moist. Absence of moisture designation indicates moisture regime is irrelevant.

R 408.31096

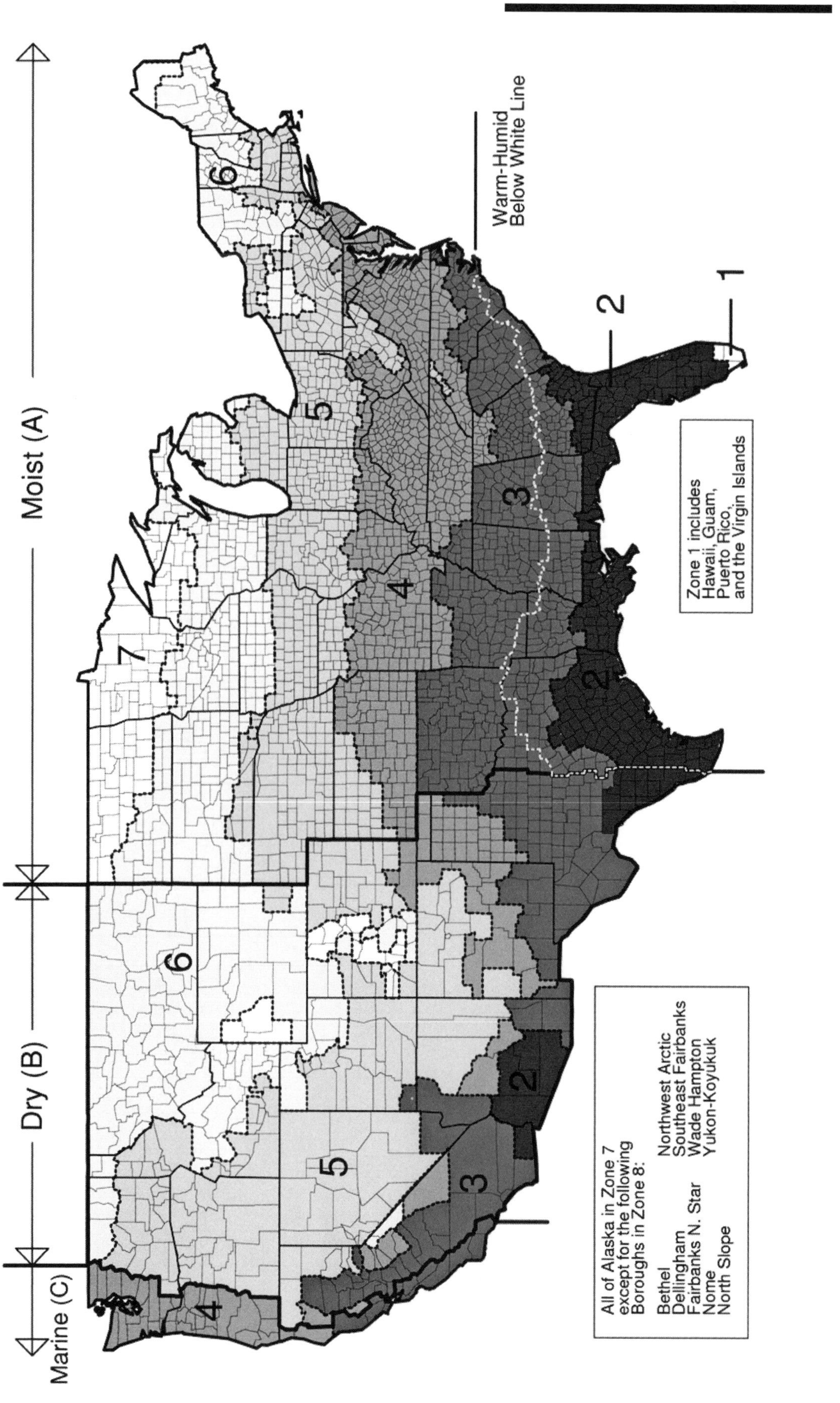
Marine (C)
Dry (B)
Moist (A)
Warm-Humid
Below White Line
All of Alaska in Zone 7
except for the following
Boroughs in Zone 8:
Bethel
Dellingham
Fairbanks N. Star
Nome
North Slope
Northwest Arctic
Southeast Fairbanks
Wade Hampton
Yukon-Koyukuk
Zone 1 includes
Hawaii, Guam,
Puerto Rico,
and the Virgin Islands
1
2
3
4
5
6
7

FIGURE C301.1
CLIMATE ZONES

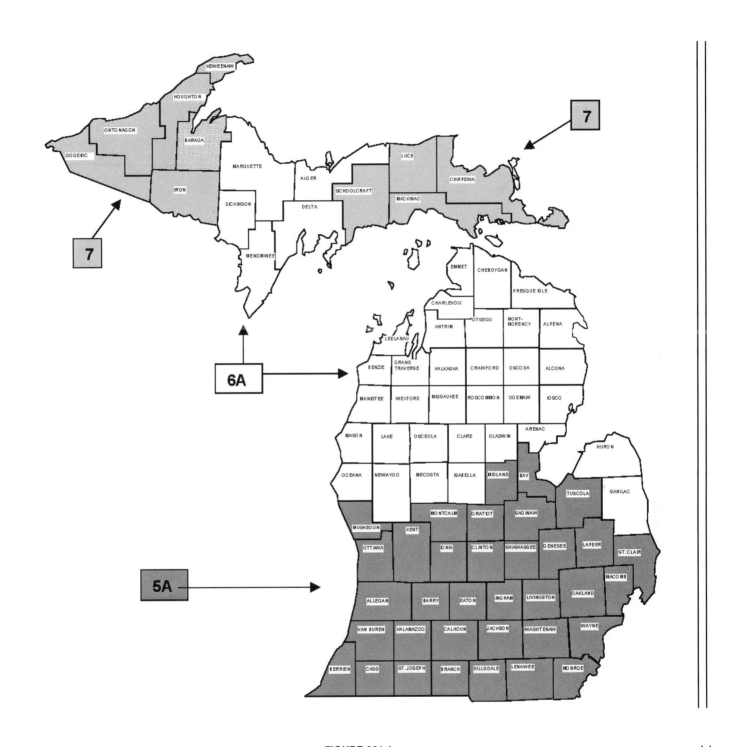

FIGURE 301.1a
CLIMATE ZONES

R 408.31096

TABLE C301.3(1)
INTERNATIONAL CLIMATE ZONE DEFINITIONS

MAJOR CLIMATE TYPE DEFINITIONS
Marine (C) Definition—Locations meeting all four criteria: 1. Mean temperature of coldest month between -3°C (27°F) and 18°C (65°F). 2. Warmest month mean < 22°C (72°F). 3. At least four months with mean temperatures over 10°C (50°F). 4. Dry season in summer. The month with the heaviest precipitation in the cold season has at least three times as much precipitation as the month with the least precipitation in the rest of the year. The cold season is October through March in the Northern Hemisphere and April through September in the Southern Hemisphere.
Dry (B) Definition—Locations meeting the following criteria: Not marine and $P_{in} < 0.44 \times (TF - 19.5)$ $[P_{cm} < 2.0 \times (TC + 7)$ in SI units] where: P_{in} = Annual precipitation in inches (cm) T = Annual mean temperature in °F (°C)
Moist (A) Definition—Locations that are not marine and not dry.
Warm-humid Definition—Moist (A) locations where either of the following wet-bulb temperature conditions shall occur during the warmest six consecutive months of the year: 1. 67°F (19.4°C) or higher for 3,000 or more hours; or 2. 73°F (22.8°C) or higher for 1,500 or more hours.

For SI: °C = [(°F)-32]/1.8, 1 inch = 2.54 cm.

TABLE C301.3(2)
CLIMATE ZONE DEFINITIONS

ZONE NUMBER	THERMAL CRITERIA	
	IP Units	SI Units
5A	5400 < HDD65°F≤7200	3000 < HDD18°C≤4000
6A	7200 < HDD65°F≤9000	4000 < HDD18°C≤5000
7	9000 < HDD65°F≤12600	5000 < HDD18°C≤7000

For SI: °C = [(°F)-32]/1.8

R 408.31096

SECTION C303
MATERIALS, SYSTEMS AND EQUIPMENT

C303.1 Identification. Materials, systems and equipment shall be identified in a manner that will allow a determination of compliance with the applicable provisions of this code.

C303.1.1 Building thermal envelope insulation. An *R*-value identification mark shall be applied by the manufacturer to each piece of *building thermal envelope* insulation 12 inches (305 mm) or greater in width. Alternately, the insulation installers shall provide a certification listing the type, manufacturer and *R*-value of insulation installed in each element of the *building thermal envelope*. For blown or sprayed insulation (fiberglass and cellulose), the initial installed thickness, settled thickness, settled *R*-value, installed density, coverage area and number of bags installed shall be *listed* on the certification. For sprayed polyurethane foam (SPF) insulation, the installed thickness of the areas covered and *R*-value of installed thickness shall be *listed* on the certification. For insulated siding, the *R*-value shall be labeled on the product's package and shall be *listed* on the certification. The insulation installer shall sign, date and post the certification in a conspicuous location on the job site.

C303.1.1.1 Blown or sprayed roof/ceiling insulation. The thickness of blown-in or sprayed roof/ceiling insulation (fiberglass or cellulose) shall be written in inches (mm) on markers that are installed at least one for every 300 square feet (28 m²) throughout the attic space. The markers shall be affixed to the trusses or joists and marked with the minimum initial installed thickness with numbers not less than 1 inch (25 mm) in height. Each marker shall face the attic access opening. Spray polyurethane foam thickness and installed *R*-value shall be *listed* on certification provided by the insulation installer.

C303.1.2 Insulation mark installation. Insulating materials shall be installed such that the manufacturer's *R*-value mark is readily observable upon inspection.

C303.1.3 Fenestration product rating. *U*-factors or fenestration products (windows, doors, and skylights) shall be determined in accordance with NFRC 100 by an accredited, independent laboratory, and labeled and certified by the manufacturer. Products lacking a labeled *U*-factor shall be assigned a default *U*-factor from Table C303.1.3(1) or C303.1.3(2).

Exceptions:

1. Computer simulations by independent NFRC certified laboratories or approval under the Stille-Derossett-Hale Single State Construction Code Act, 1972 PA 230, MCL 125.1501 to 125.1531, is considered in compliance with this section.

2. Where required, garage door *U*-factors shall be determined in accordance with either NFRC 100 or ANSI/DASMA 105.

U-factors shall be determined by an accredited, independent laboratory, and labeled and certified by the manufacturer.

Products lacking a labeled *U*-factor shall be assigned a default *U*-factor from Table C303.1.3(1) or C303.1.3(2). The solar heat gain coefficient (SHGC) and visible transmittance (VT) of glazed fenestration products (windows, glazed doors, and skylights) shall be determined in accordance with NFRC 200 by an accredited, independent laboratory, and labeled and certified by the manufacturer. Products lacking such a labeled SHGC or VT shall be assigned a default SHGC or VT from Table C303.1.3(3).

R 408.31097

TABLE C303.1.3(1)
DEFAULT GLAZED FENESTRATION *U*-FACTORS

FRAME TYPE	SINGLE PANE	DOUBLE PANE	SKYLIGHT	
			Single	Double
Metal	1.20	0.80	2.00	1.30
Metal with Thermal Break	1.10	0.65	1.90	1.10
Nonmetal or Metal Clad	0.95	0.55	1.75	1.05
Glazed Block	0.60			

TABLE C303.1.3(2)
DEFAULT DOOR *U*-FACTORS

DOOR TYPE	*U*-FACTOR
Uninsulated Metal	1.20
Insulated Metal	0.60
Wood	0.50
Insulated, nonmetal edge, max 45% glazing, any glazing double pane	0.35

TABLE C303.1.3(3)
DEFAULT GLAZED FENESTRATION SHGC AND VT

	SINGLE GLAZED		DOUBLE GLAZED		GLAZED BLOCK
	Clear	Tinted	Clear	Tinted	
SHGC	0.8	0.7	0.7	0.6	0.6
VT	0.6	0.3	0.6	0.3	0.6

C303.1.4 Insulation product rating. The thermal resistance (*R*-value) of insulation shall be determined in accordance with the U.S. Federal Trade Commission *R*-value rule (CFR Title 16, Part 460) in units of h · ft² · °F/Btu at a mean temperature of 75°F (24°C).

C303.1.4.1 Insulated siding. The thermal resistance (*R*-value) of insulated siding shall be determined in accordance with ASTM C1363. Installation for testing shall be in accordance with the manufacturer's instructions.

C303.2 Installation. Materials, systems and equipment shall be installed in accordance with the manufacturer's instructions and the *International Building Code*.

C303.2.1 Protection of exposed foundation insulation. Insulation applied to the exterior of basement walls, crawlspace walls and the perimeter of slab-on-grade floors shall have a rigid, opaque and weather-resistant protective covering to prevent the degradation of the insulation's thermal performance. The protective covering shall cover the exposed exterior insulation and extend not less than 6 inches (153 mm) below grade.

C303.3 Maintenance information. Maintenance instructions shall be furnished for equipment and systems that require preventive maintenance. Required regular maintenance actions shall be clearly stated and incorporated on a readily accessible label. The label shall include the title or publication number for the operation and maintenance manual for that particular model and type of product.

COMMERCIAL ENERGY EFFICIENCY

SECTION C401
GENERAL

C401.1 Scope. The provisions in this chapter are applicable to commercial *buildings* and their *building sites.*

C401.2 Application. Commercial buildings shall comply with the requirements of ANSI/ASHRAE/IESNA 90.1-2013.

R 408.31087b

*

EXISTING BUILDINGS

SECTION C501
GENERAL

C501.1 Scope. The requirements contained in this chapter are applicable to commercial buildings, or portions of commercial buildings. These commercial buildings shall meet the requirements of ASHRAE/IESNA Standard 90.1, "Energy Standard for Buildings Except for Low-Rise Residential Buildings, and the requirements contained in this chapter.

R 408.31087a

C501.2 Existing buildings. Except as specified in this chapter, this code shall not be used to require the removal, *alteration* or abandonment of, nor prevent the continued use and maintenance of, an existing building or building system lawfully in existence at the time of adoption of this code.

C501.3 Maintenance. Buildings and structures, and parts thereof, shall be maintained in a safe and sanitary condition. Devices and systems that are required by this code shall be maintained in conformance to the code edition under which installed. The owner or the owner's authorized agent shall be responsible for the maintenance of buildings and structures. The requirements of this chapter shall not provide the basis for removal or abrogation of energy conservation, fire protection and safety systems and devices in existing structures.

C501.4 Compliance. *Alterations*, *repairs*, *additions* and changes of occupancy to, or relocation of, existing buildings and structures shall comply with the provisions for *alterations*, *repairs*, *additions* and changes of occupancy or relocation, respectively, in the *International Building Code*, *International Fire Code*, *International Fuel Gas Code*, *International Mechanical Code*, *International Plumbing Code*, *International Property Maintenance Code*, *International Private Sewage Disposal Code* and NFPA 70.

C501.5 New and replacement materials. Except as otherwise required or permitted by this code, materials permitted by the applicable code for new construction shall be used. Like materials shall be permitted for *repairs*, provided hazards to life, health or property are not created. Hazardous materials shall not be used where the code for new construction would not permit use of these materials in buildings of similar occupancy, purpose and location.

C501.6 Historic buildings. No provisions of this code relating to the construction, *repair, alteration*, restoration and movement of structures, and *change of occupancy* shall be mandatory for *historic buildings* provided a report has been submitted to the *code official* and signed by a *registered design professional*, or a representative of the State Historic Preservation Office or the historic preservation authority having jurisdiction, demonstrating that compliance with that provision would threaten, degrade or destroy the historic form, fabric or function of the building.

SECTION C502
ADDITIONS

C502.1 Additions. Additions shall comply with ASHRAE 90.1-2013, Section 4.2.1.2.

R 408.31091

SECTION C503
ALTERATIONS

C503.1 Alterations. Alterations to any building or structure shall comply with the requirements of ASHRAE 90.1-2013, Section 4.2.1.3.

R 408.31091

SECTION C504
REPAIRS

C504.1 General. Buildings and structures, and parts thereof, shall be repaired in compliance with Section C501.3 and this section. Work on nondamaged components that is necessary for the required repair of damaged components shall be considered part of the repair and shall not be subject to the requirements for alterations in this chapter. Routine maintenance required by Section C501.3, ordinary repairs exempt from permit and abatement of wear due to normal service conditions shall not be subject to the requirements for repairs in this section.

Where a building was constructed to comply with ANSI/ASHRAE/IESNA 90.1, repairs shall comply with the standard.

R 408.31091

C504.2 Application. For the purposes of this code, the following shall be considered repairs:

1. Glass-only replacements in an existing sash and frame.

2. *Roof repairs*.

3. Air barriers shall not be required for *roof repair* where the repairs to the building do not include *alterations*, renovations or *repairs* to the remainder of the building envelope.

4. Replacement of existing doors that separate conditioned space from the exterior shall not require the installation of a vestibule or revolving door, provided that an existing vestibule that separates a conditioned space from the exterior shall not be removed.

5. *Repairs* where only the bulb, the ballast or both within the existing luminaires in a space are replaced, provided that the replacement does not increase the installed interior lighting power.

SECTION C505
CHANGE OF OCCUPANCY OR USE

C505.1 General. Spaces undergoing a change in occupancy that would result in an increase in demand for either fossil fuel or electrical energy shall comply with this code.

R 408.31091

SECTION C506
ANSI/ASHRAE/IES STANDARD 90.1-2013

C506.1 Envelope alterations.

5.1.3 Alterations to the building envelope shall comply with the requirements of Section 5 for insulation, air leakage, and fenestration applicable to those specific portions of the building that are being altered.

Exceptions:

1. Installation of storm windows or glazing panels over existing glazing, provided the storm window or glazing panel contains a low-emissivity coating. However, a low-emissivity coating is not required where the existing glazing already has a low-emissivity coating. Installation may be either on the inside or outside of the existing glazing.

2. Replacement of glazing in existing sash and frame, provided the U-factor and SHGC will be equal to or lower than before the glass replacement.

3. Alterations to roof or ceiling, wall, or floor cavities that are insulated to full depth with insulation having a minimum nominal value of R-3.0/in.

4. Alterations to walls and floors, where the existing structure is without framing cavities and no new framing cavities are created.

5. Roof recovering.

6. Removal and replacement of a roof membrane where there is existing roof insulation integral to or below the roof deck.

7. Removal and replacement of a roof membrane where the insulation is installed entirely above the roof deck, a minimum of R-20 insulation shall be permitted where the placement of additional insulation greater than R-20 insulation would require either of the following:

   a. Raising the height of parapets, weep systems, or through wall flashings where roof abuts adjoining walls or parapets.

   b. Raising the height of mechanical or electrical equipment, mechanical curbs, roof hatches, skylight curbs, service equipment, piping, conduit, duct work, roof platforms, ladders, stairs, guard rails, expansion joints, roof davits, or door thresholds.

8. Replacement of existing fenestration, provided that the area of the replacement fenestration does not exceed 25% of the total fenestration area of an existing building and that the U-factor and SHGC will be

equal to or lower than before the fenestration replacement.

R 408.31098

C506.2 Vestibules.

5.4.3.4 Vestibules. Building entrances that separate conditioned space from the exterior shall be protected with an enclosed vestibule, with all doors opening into and out of the vestibule equipped with self-closing devices. Vestibules shall be designed so that in passing through the vestibule it is not necessary for the interior and exterior doors to open at the same time. Interior and exterior doors shall have a minimum distance between them of not less than 7 feet when in the closed positon. The floor area of each vestibule shall not exceed the greater of 50 feet^2 or 2% of the gross conditioned floor area for that level of the building. The exterior envelope of conditioned vestibules shall comply with the requirements for a conditioned space. The interior and exterior envelope of unconditioned vestibules shall comply with the requirements for a semiheated space.

Exceptions:

1. Doors not intended to be used by the public, such as doors to storage, mechanical, electrical, or equipment rooms.

2. Doors opening directly from a sleeping unit or dwelling unit.

3. Doors that open directly from a space less than 3,000 feet^2 (298 m^2) in area.

4. Revolving doors.

5. Doors used primarily to facilitate shipping, receiving, or material handling.

6. Doors with no exterior entrance hardware.

7. Doors leading solely to outdoor eating areas.

8. Overhead doors.

R 408.31098a

C506.3 System commissioning.

6.7.2.4 System commissioning. HVAC control systems shall be tested to ensure that control elements are calibrated, adjusted, and in proper working condition. For projects larger than 10,000 ft^2, conditioned area, except warehouses and semiheated spaces, detailed instructions for commissioning HVAC systems (see informative appendix E) shall be provided by the designer in plans and specifications.

R 408.31098b

C506.4 Lighting alterations.

9.1.2 Lighting alterations. For the alteration of any lighting system in an interior space, that space shall comply with the lighting power density (LPD) requirements of section 9 applicable to that space and the automatic shutoff requirements of Section 9.4.1.1. For the alteration of any lighting system in an exterior building application, that lighting system shall comply with the lighting power density (LPD) requirements of Section 9 applicable to the area illuminated by that lighting system and the applicable control requirements of Sections 9.4.1.4(a) and 9.4.1.4(b). These alterations shall include all luminaires that are added, replaced, or removed. This requirement shall also be met for alterations that involve only the replacement of lamps plus ballasts. Alterations do not include routine maintenance or repair situations.

Exception: Alterations that involve less than 50% of the connected lighting load in a space or area do not have to comply with these requirements, provided that such alterations do not increase the installed LPD.

R 408.31098c

CHAPTER 6 [CE]

REFERENCED STANDARDS

This chapter lists the standards that are referenced in various sections of this document. The standards are listed herein by the promulgating agency of the standard, the standard identification, the effective date and title, and the section or sections of this document that reference the standard. The application of the referenced standards shall be as specified in Section 106.

ASHRAE
American Society of Heating, Refrigerating and Air-Conditioning Engineers, Inc.
1791 Tullie Circle, NE
Atlanta, GA 30329-2305

Standard reference number	Title	Referenced in code section number
90.1—2013	Energy Standard for Buildings Except Low-rise Residential Buildings	C401.2, C502.1, C503.1, C504.1

DASMA
Door and Access Systems Manufacturers Association
1300 Sumner Avenue
Cleveland, OH 44115-2851

Standard reference number	Title	Referenced in code section number
105—92 (R2004)—13	Test Method for Thermal Transmittance and Air Infiltration of Garage Doors	C303.1.3

ICC
International Code Council, Inc.
500 New Jersey Avenue, NW
6th Floor
Washington, DC 20001

Standard reference number	Title	Referenced in code section number
IBC—15	International Building Code®	C201.3, C303.2, C501.4
IFC—15	International Fire Code®	C201.3, C501.4
IFGC—15	International Fuel Gas Code®	C201.3, C501.4
IMC—15	International Mechanical Code®	C501.4
IPC—15	International Plumbing Code®	C201.3, C501.4
IMPC—15	International Property Maintenance Code®	C501.4
IPSDC—15	International Private Sewage Disposal Code®	C501.4

IES
Illuminating Engineering Society
120 Wall Street, 17th Floor
New York, NY 10005-4001

Standard reference number	Title	Referenced in code section number
ANSI/ASHRAE/IESNA 90.1—2013	Energy Standard for Buildings, Except Low-rise Residential Buildings	C401.2, C502.1, C503.1, C504.1

NEMA

National Electrical Manufacturers Association
1300 North 17th Street, Suite 1752
Rosslyn, VA 22209

Standard reference number	Title	Referenced in code section number
MG1—1993	Motors and Generators C202

NFPA

National Fire Protection Association
1 Batterymarch Park
Quincy, MA 02169-7471

Standard reference number	Title	Referenced in code section number
70—14	National Electrical Code C501.4

NFRC

National Fenestration Rating Council, Inc.
6305 Ivy Lane, Suite 140
Greenbelt, MD 20770

Standard reference number	Title	Referenced in code section number
100—2009	Procedure for Determining Fenestration Products U-factors—Second Edition C303.1.3
200—2009	Procedure for Determining Fenestration Product Solar Heat Gain Coefficients and Visible Transmittance at Normal Incidence—Second Edition C303.1.3
400—2009	Procedure for Determining Fenestration Product Air Leakage—Second Edition

US-FTC

United States-Federal Trade Commission
600 Pennsylvania Avenue NW
Washington, DC 20580

Standard reference number	Title	Referenced in code section number
CFR Title 16 (May 31, 2005)	R-value Rule C303.1.4

INDEX

REFRIGERATED WAREHOUSE COOLER
Defined C202

REFRIGERATED WAREHOUSE FREEZER
Defined C202

REGISTERED DESIGN PROFESSIONAL
Defined C202

**RENEWABLE/NONDEPLETABLE
ENERGY SOURCES**

REPAIR
Defined C202
Historic buildings C501.6
Requirements C501.5, C504

REPLACEMENT MATERIALS. C501.5

REROOFING
Defined C202

RESIDENTIAL BUILDINGS
Compliance C101.2, C101.4.1, C101.5
Defined C202

ROOF ASSEMBLY
Defined C202
Recover C503.1
Repairs C504.1
Requirements C303.1.1.1

ROOF RECOVER
Defined C202

ROOF REPAIR
Defined C202
Exemption C504.1

ROOF REPLACEMENT
Defined C202

ROOFTOP MONITOR
Defined C202

**ROOF VENTILATORS
(see POWERED ROOF/ WALL VENTILATORS)**

S

SATURATED CONDENSING TEMPERATURE
Defined C202
SCOPE OF CODE C101.2
SCREW LAMP HOLDERS
Defined C202
SERVICE WATER HEATING
Defined C202
Existing buildings C504.1
**SHGC
(see SOLAR HEAT GAIN COEFFICIENT)**
SKYLIGHTS
Defined (see Fenestration) C202
SLAB-EDGE INSULATION C303.2.1
SLEEPING UNIT
Defined C202

SMALL ELECTRIC MOTOR
Defined. C202
**SOLAR HEAT GAIN COEFFICIENT
(SHGC)** . . . . C103.2, Table C303.1.3(3)
Defined. C202
STANDARD REFERENCE DESIGN
Defined. C202
STANDARDS, REFERENCED. . . . . . C106, Chapter 6
STOP WORK ORDER C108
STOREFRONT
Defined. C202

T

THERMAL CONDUCTANCE (see C-Factor)
THERMAL MASS (see MASS)
THERMAL RESISTANCE (see R-VALUE)
THERMAL TRANSMITTANCE (see U-FACTOR)
THERMOSTAT
Defined. C202
TIME SWITCH CONTROL
Defined. C202

U

U-FACTOR
Default door . . . . .Table C303.1.3(2)
Default glazed fenestration . . . . . .Table C303.1.3(1)
Defined. C202

V

VARIABLE REFRIGERANT FLOW SYSTEM
Defined. C202
VENTILATION C403.2.6
Defined. C202
VENTILATION AIR
Defined. C202
**VERTICAL FENESTRATION
(see FENESTRATION)**
VISIBLE TRANSMITTANCE (VT)
Default glazed fenestration . . . . . .Table C303.1.3(3)
Defined. C202

W

WALK-IN COOLER
Defined. C202
WALK-IN FREEZER
Defined. C202
WALL
Above-grade wall, defined C202

Z

IECC—RESIDENTIAL PROVISIONS

TABLE OF CONTENTS

ENERGY EFFICIENCY

SECTION R101
SCOPE AND GENERAL REQUIREMENTS

This chapter regulates the energy efficiency for the design and construction of buildings regulated by this code.

Note: The text of the following Sections R101.3 through R105 is extracted from the 2012 edition of the International Energy Conservation Code—Residential Provisions and has been editorially revised to conform to the scope and application of this code. The section numbers appearing in parenthesis after each section number are the section numbers of the corresponding text in the International Energy Conservation Code—Residential Provisions.

R101.1 Title. This code shall be known and cited as the "Michigan Energy Code." It is referred to herein as "this code."

R 408.31060

R101.3 Intent. This code shall regulate the design and construction of buildings for the effective use and conservation of energy over the useful life of each building. This code is intended to provide flexibility to permit the use of innovative approaches and techniques to achieve this objective. This code is not intended to abridge safety, health or environmental requirements contained in other applicable codes or ordinances.

> **R101.4.3 Additions, alterations, renovations, or repairs.** Additions, alterations, renovations, or repairs to an existing building, building system, or portion thereof shall conform to the provisions of this code as they relate to new construction without requiring the unaltered portion(s) of the existing building or building system to comply with this code. Additions, alterations, renovations, or repairs shall not create an unsafe or hazardous condition or overload existing building systems. An addition shall be deemed to comply with this code if the addition alone complies or if the existing building and addition comply with this code as a single building.
>
> **Exception:** The following are exempt provided the energy use of the building is not increased:
>
> 1. Storm windows installed over existing fenestration.
>
> 2. Glass only replacements in an existing sash and frame.
>
> 3. Existing ceiling, wall, or floor cavities exposed during construction provided that these cavities are filled with insulation.
>
> 4. Construction where the existing roof, wall, or floor cavity is not exposed.
>
> 5. Reroofing where the roof is part of the thermal envelope, and where neither the roof sheathing nor the roof insulation is exposed.
>
> 6. Reroofing where the roof is not part of the thermal envelope.
>
> 7. Replacement of existing doors that separate conditioned space from the exterior shall not require the installation of a vestibule or revolving door, provided, however, that an existing vestibule that separates a conditioned space from the exterior shall not be removed.
>
> 8. Alterations that replace less than 50% of the luminaries in a space, provided that such alterations do not increase the installed interior lighting power.
>
> 9. Alterations that replace only the bulb and ballast within the existing luminaries in a space provided that the alteration does not increase the installed interior lighting power.

R408.31060

R101.4.5 Change in space conditioning. Any nonconditioned space that is altered to become *conditioned space* shall be required to be brought into full compliance with this chapter.

R101.5.1 Compliance materials. The *building official* shall be permitted to approve specific computer software, worksheets, compliance manuals and other similar materials that meet the intent of this code.

R101.5.2 Low-energy buildings. The following buildings, or portions thereof, separated from the remainder of the building by *building thermal envelope* assemblies complying with this code shall be exempt from the *building thermal envelope* provisions of this code:

1. Those with a peak design rate of energy usage less than 3.4 Btu/h · ft^2 (10.7 W/m^2) or 1.0 watt/ft^2 (10.7 W/m^2) of floor area for space conditioning purposes.

2. Those that do not contain *conditioned space*.

SECTION R102
ALTERNATE MATERIALS—
METHOD OF CONSTRUCTION, DESIGN
OR INSULATING SYSTEMS

R102.1.1 Above code programs. The state construction code commission may evaluate and approve a national, state or local energy efficiency program to exceed the energy efficiency required by this code. Buildings approved in writing by such an energy efficiency program, such as ICC 700-2012 "silver" or energy star version 3 (rev. 07) shall be considered in compliance with this code. The requirements identified as "mandatory" in chapter shall be met.

R 408.31060

SECTION R103
CONSTRUCTION DOCUMENTS

R103.1 Submittal documents. Construction documents, special inspection and structural programs, and other data shall meet both of the following requirements:

(1) Be submitted in 1 or more sets with each application for a permit.

(2) Be prepared by, or under the direct supervision of, a registered design professional when required by the Occupational Code, 1980 PA 299, MCL 339.101 to 339.2919.

Where special conditions exist, the building official may require additional construction documents to be prepared by a registered design professional.

R 408.31060a

R103.2 Information on construction documents. Construction documents shall be drawn to scale upon suitable material. Electronic media documents are permitted to be submitted when *approved* by the *building official*. Construction documents shall be of sufficient clarity to indicate the location, nature and extent of the work proposed, and show in sufficient detail pertinent data and features of the building, systems and equipment as herein governed. Details shall include, but are not limited to, as applicable, insulation materials and their *R*-values; fenestration *U*-factors and s; area-weighted *U*-factor and SHGC calculations; mechanical system design criteria; mechanical and service water heating system and equipment types, sizes and efficiencies; economizer description; equipment and systems controls; fan motor horsepower (hp) and controls; duct sealing, duct and pipe insulation and location; lighting fixture schedule with wattage and control narrative; and air sealing details.

R107.1 Payment of fees. The fees prescribed by the act shall be paid to the enforcing agency of the jurisdiction before a permit to begin work for new construction, alteration, removal, demolition, or other building operation may be issued. In addition, an amendment to a permit necessitating an additional fee shall not be approved until the additional fee has been paid.

R 408.31060b

SECTION R109
BOARD OF APPEAL

R109.1 Means of appeal.

(1) An interested person may appeal a decision of the enforcing agency to the board of appeals in accordance with the act. An application for appeal shall be based on both of the following:

(a) A claim that the true intent of the code or the rules governing construction have been incorrectly interpreted.

(b) The provisions of the code do not apply, or an equal or better form of construction is proposed.

(2) The decision of a local board of appeals may be appealed to the construction code commission in accordance with the act and time frames.

Exception: Requests for barrier free design exception shall be in accordance with 1966 PA 1, MCL 125.1352 to 125.1356.

R 408.31060c

R109.3 Qualifications. The board of appeals shall consist of members who are qualified in accordance with the act.

R 408.31060c

SECTION R202
GENERAL DEFINITIONS

R202 Defined terms. The following words and terms shall, for the purposes of this chapter, have the meanings shown herein.

ABOVE-GRADE WALL. A wall more than 50 percent above grade and enclosing *conditioned space*. This includes between-floor spandrels, peripheral edges of floors, roof and basement knee walls, dormer walls, gable end walls, walls enclosing a mansard roof and skylight shafts.

ACCESSIBLE. Admitting close approach as a result of not being guarded by locked doors, elevation or other effective means (see "Readily *accessible*").

ADDITION. An extension or increase in the *conditioned space* floor area or height of a building or structure.

AIR BARRIER. Material(s) assembled and joined together to provide a barrier to air leakage through the building envelope. An air barrier may be a single material or a combination of materials.

AUTOMATIC. Self-acting, operating by its own mechanism when actuated by some impersonal influence, as, for example, a change in current strength, pressure, temperature or mechanical configuration (see "Manual").

BASEMENT WALL. A wall 50 percent or more below grade and enclosing *conditioned space*.

BUILDING. "Building" as defined in the Stille-DeRossett-Hale Single State Construction Code Act, 1972 PA 230, MCL 125.1501 to 125.1531.

R 408.31060d

BUILDING OFFICIAL. The person who is appointed and employed by a governmental subdivision, who is charged with the administration and enforcement of the state codes specified in R 408.30499 of the *Michigan Building Code*, and who is registered in accordance with the requirements of 1986 PA 54, MCL 338.2301 to 338.2313.

R 408.31060d

BUILDING SITE. A contiguous area of land that is under the ownership or control of one entity.

BUILDING THERMAL ENVELOPE. The basement walls, exterior walls, floor, roof, and any other building elements that enclose *conditioned space* or provides a boundary between *conditioned space* and exempt or unconditioned space.

C-FACTOR (THERMAL CONDUCTANCE). The coefficient of heat transmission (surface to surface) through a building component or assembly, equal to the time rate of heat flow per unit area and the unit temperature difference between the warm side and cold side surfaces (Btu/h · ft^2 · °F) [W/(m^2 · K)].

CONDITIONED FLOOR AREA. The horizontal projection of the floors associated with the *conditioned space*.

CONDITIONED SPACE. An area or room within a building being heated or cooled, containing uninsulated ducts, or with a fixed opening directly into an adjacent *conditioned space*.

CONTINUOUS AIR BARRIER. A combination of materials and assemblies that restrict or prevent the passage of air through the building thermal envelope.

CRAWL SPACE WALL. The opaque portion of a wall that encloses a crawl space and is partially or totally below grade.

CURTAIN WALL. Fenestration products used to create an external nonload-bearing wall that is designed to separate the exterior and interior environments.

DEMAND RECIRCULATION WATER SYSTEM. A water distribution system where pump(s) prime the service hot water piping with heated water upon demand for hot water.

DUCT. A tube or conduit utilized for conveying air. The air passages of self-contained systems are not to be construed as air ducts.

DUCT SYSTEM. A continuous passageway for the transmission of air that, in addition to ducts, includes duct fittings, dampers, plenums, fans and accessory air-handling equipment and appliances.

ENERGY ANALYSIS. A method for estimating the annual energy use of the *proposed design* and *standard reference design* based on estimates of energy use.

ENERGY COST. The total estimated annual cost for purchased energy for the building functions regulated by this code, including applicable demand charges.

ENERGY SIMULATION TOOL. An *approved* software program or calculation-based methodology that projects the annual energy use of a building.

ENTRANCE DOOR. Fenestration products used for ingress, egress and access in nonresidential buildings, including, but not limited to, exterior entrances that utilize latching hardware and automatic closers and contain over 50-percent glass specifically designed to withstand heavy use and possibly abuse.

EXTERIOR WALL. Walls including both above-grade walls and basement walls.

FENESTRATION. Skylights, roof windows, vertical windows (fixed or moveable), opaque doors, glazed doors, glazed block and combination opaque/glazed doors. Fenestration includes products with glass and nonglass glazing materials.

FENESTRATION PRODUCT, SITE-BUILT. A fenestration designed to be made up of field-glazed or field-assembled units using specific factory cut or otherwise factory-formed framing and glazing units. Examples of site-built fenestration include storefront systems, curtain walls, and atrium roof systems.

HEATED SLAB. Slab-on-grade construction in which the heating elements, hydronic tubing, or hot air distribution system is in contact with, or placed within or under, the slab.

HIGH-EFFICACY LAMPS. Compact fluorescent lamps, T-8 or smaller diameter linear fluorescent lamps, or lamps with a minimum efficacy of:

1. 60 lumens per watt for lamps over 40 watts;
2. 50 lumens per watt for lamps over 15 watts to 40 watts; and
3. 40 lumens per watt for lamps 15 watts or less.

INFILTRATION. The uncontrolled inward air leakage into a building caused by the pressure effects of wind or the effect of differences in the indoor and outdoor air density or both.

INSULATING SHEATHING. An insulating board with a core material having a minimum *R*-value of R-2.

LOW-VOLTAGE LIGHTING. Lighting equipment powered through a transformer such as a cable conductor, a rail conductor and track lighting.

MANUAL. Capable of being operated by personal intervention (see "Automatic").

PROPOSED DESIGN. A description of the proposed building used to estimate annual energy use for determining compliance based on total building performance.

READILY ACCESSIBLE. Capable of being reached quickly for operation, renewal or inspection without requiring those to whom ready access is requisite to climb over or remove obstacles or to resort to portable ladders or access equipment (see "Accessible").

REPAIR. The reconstruction or renewal of any part of an existing building.

RESIDENTIAL BUILDING. For this code, includes detached one- and two-family dwellings and multiple single-family dwellings (townhouses) as well as Group R-2, R-3 and R-4 buildings three stories or less in height above grade plane.

R-VALUE (THERMAL RESISTANCE). The inverse of the time rate of heat flow through a body from one of its bounding surfaces to the other surface for a unit temperature difference between the two surfaces, under steady state conditions, per unit area (h · ft^2 · °F/Btu) [(m^2 · K)/W].

SERVICE WATER HEATING. Supply of hot water for pur- poses other than comfort heating.

SKYLIGHT. Glass or other transparent or translucent glazing material installed at a slope of less than 60 degrees (1.05 rad) from horizontal. Glazing material in skylights, including unit skylights, solariums, sunrooms, roofs and sloped walls is included in this definition.

SOLAR HEAT GAIN COEFFICIENT (SHGC). The ratio of the solar heat gain entering the space through the fenestration assembly to the incident solar radiation. Solar heat gain includes directly transmitted solar heat and absorbed solar radiation which is then reradiated, conducted or convected into the space.

STANDARD REFERENCE DESIGN. A version of the *proposed design* that meets the minimum requirements of this code and is used to determine the maximum annual energy use requirement for compliance based on total building performance.

SUNROOM. A one-story structure attached to a dwelling with a glazing area in excess of 40 percent of the gross area of the structure's exterior walls and roof.

THERMAL ISOLATION. Physical and space conditioning separation from *conditioned space(s)*. The *conditioned space*(s) shall be controlled as separate zones for heating and cooling or conditioned by separate equipment.

THERMOSTAT. An automatic control device used to maintain temperature at a fixed or adjustable set point.

U-**FACTOR (THERMAL TRANSMITTANCE).** The coefficient of heat transmission (air to air) through a building component or assembly, equal to the time rate of heat flow per unit area and unit temperature difference between the warm side and cold side air films (Btu/h $\cdot$ ft^2 $\cdot$ °F) [W/(m^2 $\cdot$ K)].

VENTILATION AIR. That portion of supply air that comes from outside (outdoors) plus any recirculated air that has been treated to maintain the desired quality of air within a designated space.

VISIBLE TRANSMITTANCE [VT]. The ratio of visible light entering the space through the fenestration product assembly to the incident visible light, visible transmittance, includes the effects of glazing material and frame and is expressed as a number between 0 and 1.

WHOLE HOUSE MECHANICAL VENTILATION SYSTEM. An exhaust system, supply system, or combination thereof that is designed to mechanically exchange indoor air with outdoor air when operating continuously or through a programmed intermittent schedule to satisfy the whole house ventilation rates.

ZONE. A space or group of spaces within a building with heating or cooling requirements that are sufficiently similar so that desired conditions can be maintained throughout using a single controlling device.

SECTION R301
CLIMATE ZONES

R301.1 General. Climate zones from Figures 301.1, 301.1a or Table 301.1 shall be used in determining the applicable requirements of this code.

R408.31060e

SECTION R302
DESIGN CONDITIONS

R302.1 Interior design conditions. The interior design temperatures used for heating and cooling load calculations shall be a maximum of 72°F (22°C) for heating and minimum of 75°F (24°C) for cooling.

SECTION R303
MATERIALS, SYSTEMS AND EQUIPMENT

R303.1 Identification. Materials, systems and equipment shall be identified in a manner that will allow a determination of compliance with the applicable provisions of this code.

R303.1.1 Building thermal envelope insulation. An *R*-value identification mark shall be applied by the manufacturer to each piece of *building thermal envelope* insulation 12 inches (305 mm) or greater in width. Alternately, the insulation installers shall provide a certification listing the type, manufacturer and *R*-value of insulation installed in each element of the *building thermal envelope*. For blown or sprayed insulation (fiberglass and cellulose), the initial installed thickness, settled thickness, settled *R*-value, installed density, coverage area and number of bags installed shall be *listed* on the certification. For sprayed polyurethane foam (SPF) insulation, the installed thickness of the areas covered and *R*-value of installed thickness shall be *listed* on the certification. The insulation installer shall sign, date and post the certification in a conspicuous location on the job site.

R303.1.1.1 Blown or sprayed roof/ceiling insulation. The thickness of blown-in or sprayed roof/ceiling insulation (fiberglass or cellulose) shall be written in inches (mm) on markers that are installed at least one for every 300 square feet (28 m^2) throughout the attic space. The markers shall be affixed to the trusses or joists and marked with the minimum initial installed thickness with numbers a minimum of 1 inch (25 mm) in height. Each marker shall face the attic access opening. Spray polyurethane foam thickness and installed *R*-value shall be *listed* on certification provided by the insulation installer.

R303.1.2 Insulation mark installation. Insulating materials shall be installed such that the manufacturer's *R*-value mark is readily observable upon inspection.

R303.1.3 Fenestration product rating. *U*-factors of fenestration products (windows, doors and skylights) shall be determined in accordance with NFRC 100 by an accredited, independent laboratory, and labeled and certified by the manufacturer. Products lacking such a labeled *U*-factor shall be assigned a default *U*-factor from Table R303.1.3(1) or R303.1.3(2).

Exception: Computer simulations by independent NFRC certified laboratories or approval under section 21 of 1972 PA 230, MCL 125.1521 are considered in compliance with this section.

R408.31062

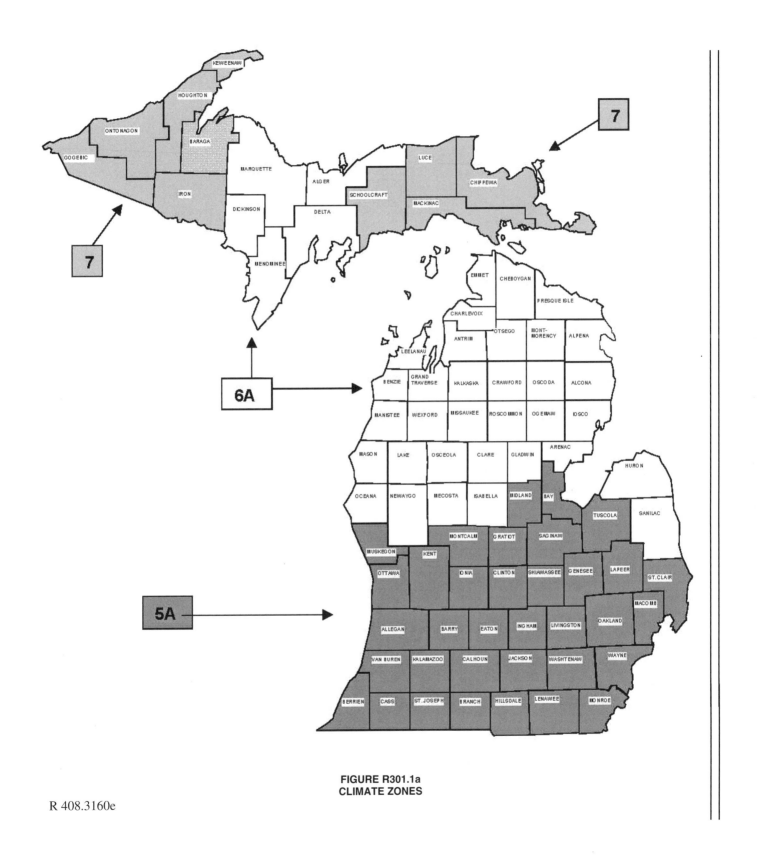

**FIGURE R301.1a
CLIMATE ZONES**

R 408.3160e

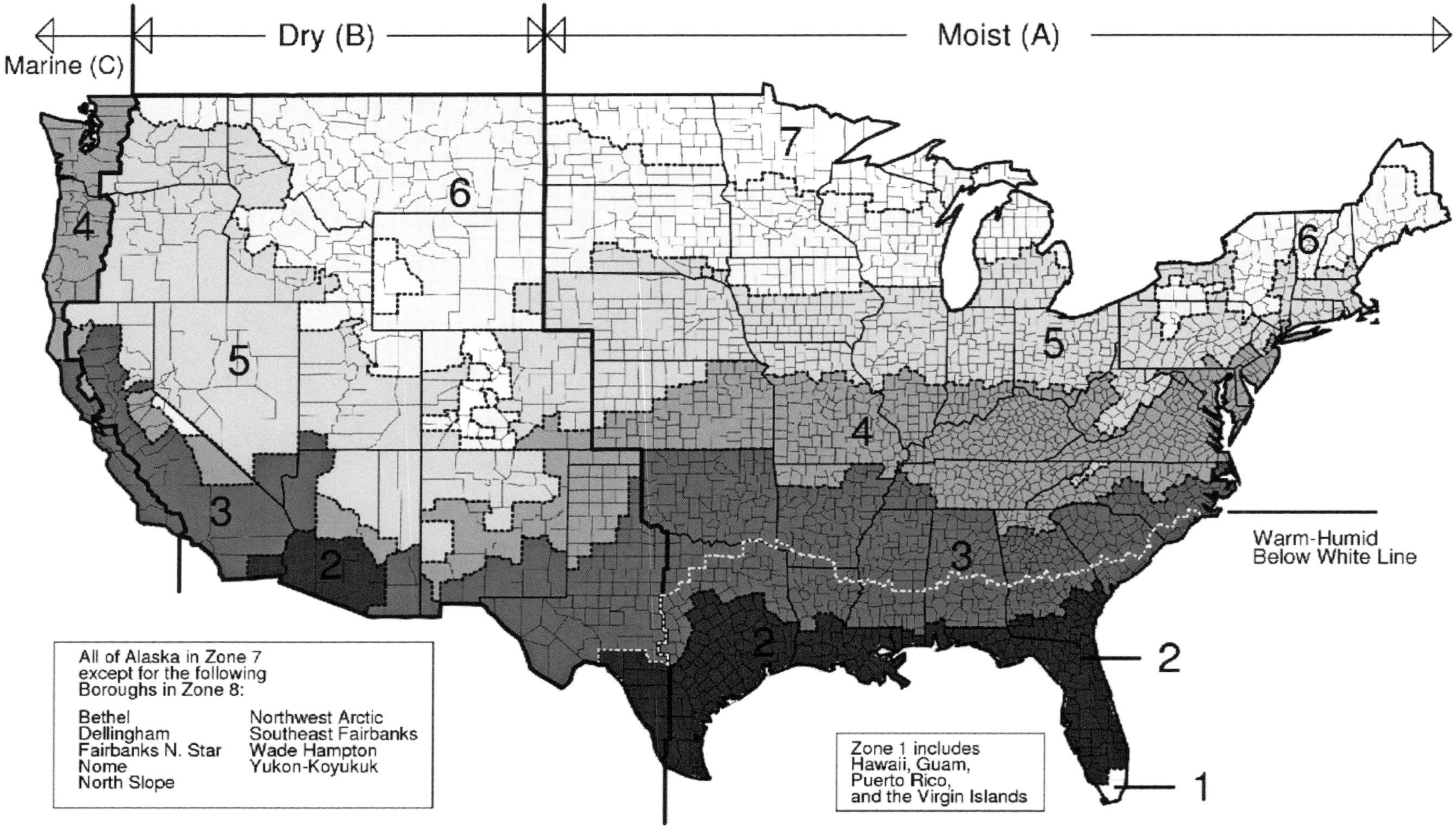

**FIGURE R301.1
CLIMATE ZONES**

Moist (A)

Dry (B)

Marine (C)

Warm-Humid
Below White Line

Zone 1 includes
Hawaii, Guam,
Puerto Rico,
and the Virgin Islands

All of Alaska in Zone 7
except for the following
Boroughs in Zone 8:

Bethel   Northwest Arctic
Dellingham   Southeast Fairbanks
Fairbanks N. Star   Wade Hampton
Nome   Yukon-Koyukuk
North Slope

TABLE R301.1
CLIMATE ZONES BY COUNTY

ZONES		
5A	**6A**	**7**
Allegan	Alcona	Baraga
Barry	Alger	Chippewa
Bay	Alpena	Gogebic
Berrien	Antrim	Houghton
Branch	Arenac	Iron
Calhoun	Benzie	Keweenaw
Cass	Charlevoix	Luce
Clinton	Cheboygan	Mackinac
Eaton	Clare	Ontonagon
Genesee	Crawford	Schoolcraft
Gratiot	Delta	
Hillsdale	Dickinson	
Ingham	Emmet	
Ionia	Gladwin	
Jackson	Grand Traverse	
Kalamazoo	Huron	
Kent	Iosco	
Lapeer	Isabella	
Lenawee	Kalkaska	
Livingston	Lake	
Macomb	Leelanau	
Midland	Manistee	
Monroe	Marquette	
Montcalm	Mason	
Muskegon	Mecosta	
Oakland	Menominee	
Ottawa	Missaukee	
Saginaw	Montmorency	
Shiawassee	Newaygo	
St. Clair	Oceana	
St. Joseph	Ogemaw	
Tuscola	Osceola	
Van Buren	Oscoda	
Washtenaw	Otsego	
Wayne	Presque Isle	
	Roscommon	
	Sanilac	
	Wexford	

Key: A – Moist. Absence of moisture designation indicates moisture regime is irrelevant.

R408.31060e

TABLE R301.3(2)
CLIMATE ZONE DEFINITIONS

ZONE NUMBER	THERMAL CRITERIA	
	IP Units	SI Units
5A	$5400 < HDD65°F \leq 7200$	$3000 < HDD18°C \leq 4000$
6A	$7200 < HDD65°F \leq 9000$	$4000 < HDD18°C \leq 5000$
7	$9000 < HDD65°F \leq 12600$	$5000 < HDD18°C \leq 7000$

For SI: °C = [(°F)-32]/1.8.

R408.31060e

TABLE R302.3(1)
INTERNATIONAL CLIMATE ZONE DEFINITIONS

MAJOR CLIMATE TYPE DEFINITIONS
Marine (C) Definition—Locations meeting all four criteria: 1. Mean temperature of coldest month between -3°C (27°F) and 18°C (65°F).   2. Warmest month mean < 22°C (72°F).   3. At least four months with mean temperatures over 10°C (50°F).   4. Dry season in summer. The month with the heaviest precipitation in the cold season has at least three times as much precipitation as the month with the least precipitation in the rest of the year. The cold season is October through March in the Northern Hemisphere and April through September in the Southern Hemisphere.

Dry (B) Definition—Locations meeting the following criteria:
 Not marine and $P_{in} < 0.44 \times (TF - 19.5)$ $[P_{cm} < 2.0 \times (TC + 7)$ in SI units]
 where:
     P_{in} = Annual precipitation in inches (cm)
     T = Annual mean temperature in °F (°C)

Moist (A) Definition—Locations that are not marine and not dry.
Warm-humid Definition—Moist (A) locations where either of the following wet-bulb temperature conditions shall occur during the warmest six consecutive months of the year: 1. 67°F (19.4°C) or higher for 3,000 or more hours; or   2. 73°F (22.8°C) or higher for 1,500 or more hours.

For SI: °C = [(°F)-32]/1.8, 1 inch = 2.54 cm.

TABLE R303.1.3(1)
DEFAULT GLAZED FENESTRATION U-FACTOR

FRAME TYPE	SINGLE PANE	DOUBLE PANE	SKYLIGHT	
			Single	Double
Metal	1.20	0.80	2.00	1.30
Metal with Thermal Break	1.10	0.65	1.90	1.10
Nonmetal or Metal Clad	0.95	0.55	1.75	1.05
Glazed Block	0.60			

TABLE R303.1.3(2)
DEFAULT DOOR U-FACTORS

DOOR TYPE	U-FACTOR
Uninsulated Metal	1.20
Insulated Metal	0.60
Wood	0.50
Insulated, nonmetal edge, max 45% glazing, any glazing double pane	0.35

R303.1.4 Insulation product rating. The thermal resistance (R-value) of insulation shall be determined in accordance with the U.S. Federal Trade Commission R-value rule (CFR Title 16, Part 460) in units of h × ft² × °F/Btu at a mean temperature of 75°F (24°C).

R303.2 Installation. All materials, systems and equipment shall be installed in accordance with the manufacturer's installation instructions and this code.

R303.2.1 Protection of exposed foundation insulation. Insulation applied to the exterior of basement walls, crawl-space walls and the perimeter of slab-on-grade floors shall have a rigid, opaque and weather-resistant protective covering to prevent the degradation of the insulation's thermal performance. The protective covering shall cover the exposed exterior insulation and extend a minimum of 6 inches (153 mm) below grade.

R303.3 Maintenance information. Maintenance instructions shall be furnished for equipment and systems that require preventive maintenance. Required regular maintenance actions shall be clearly stated and incorporated on a readily accessible label. The label shall include the title or publication number for the operation and maintenance manual for that particular model and type of product.

SECTION 401
GENERAL

R401.2 Compliance. Projects shall comply with Sections identified as "mandatory" and with either sections identified as "prescriptive" or the performance approach in Section R405.

R401.3 Certificate (mandatory). A permanent certificate shall be posted on or in the electrical distribution panel, and shall meet all of the following:

(a) Be affixed or attached so it does not cover or obstruct the visibility of the circuit directory label, service disconnect label, or other required labels.

(b) Be completed by the builder or registered design professional.

(c) List the predominant *R*-values of insulation installed in or on ceiling/roof, walls, foundation (slab, basement wall, crawlspace wall and/or floor) and ducts outside conditioned spaces and *U*-factors for fenestration. If there is more than 1 value for each component, then the certificate shall list the value covering the largest area.

(d) List the types and efficiencies of heating, cooling and service water heating equipment.

(e) If a gas-fired unvented room heater, electric furnace, or baseboard electric heater is installed in the residence, then the certificate shall list "gas-fired unvented room heater," as appropriate. An efficiency shall not be listed for gas-fired unvented room heaters, electric furnaces, or electric baseboard heaters.

R408.31061

SECTION R402
BUILDING THERMAL ENVELOPE

R402.1 General (Prescriptive). The *building thermal envelope* shall meet the requirements of Sections R402.1.1 through R402.1.4.

R402.1.1 Insulation and fenestration criteria. The *building thermal envelope* shall meet the requirements of Table R402.1.1 based on the climate zone specified in Section R301.10.

R402.1.2 *R*-value computation. Insulation material used in layers, such as framing cavity insulation and insulating sheathing, shall be summed to compute the component *R*-value. The manufacturer's settled *R*-value shall be used for blown insulation. Computed *R*-values shall not include an *R*-value for other building materials or air films.

R402.1.3 *U*-factor alternative. An assembly with a *U*-factor equal to or less than that specified in Table R402.1.3 shall be permitted as an alternative to the *R*-value in Table R402.1.1.

R402.1.4 Total UA alternative. If the total *building thermal envelope* UA (sum of *U*-factor times assembly area) is less than or equal to the total UA resulting from using the U-factors in Table R402.1.3 (multiplied by the same assembly area as in the proposed building), the building shall be considered in compliance with Table R402.1.1. The UA calculation shall be done using a method consistent with the ASHRAE *Handbook of Fundamentals* and shall include the thermal bridging effects of framing materials.

R 408.31065

R402.2 Specific insulation requirements (Prescriptive). In addition to the requirements of Section R402.1, insulation shall meet the specific requirements of Sections R402.2.1 through R402.2.12.

TABLE R402.1.1
INSULATION AND FENESTRATION REQUIREMENTS BY COMPONENT[a]

CLIMATE ZONE	FENESTRATION *U*-FACTOR[b]	SKYLIGHT[b] *U*-FACTOR	CEILING *R*-VALUE	WOOD FRAME WALL *R*-VALUE	MASS WALL *R*-VALUE[g]	FLOOR *R*-VALUE	BASEMENT[c] WALL *R*-VALUE	SLAB[d] *R*-VALUE & DEPTH	CRAWL SPACE[c] WALL *R*-VALUE
5A	0.32	0.55	38	20 or 13 + 5[f]	13/17	30[e]	10/13	10, 2 ft	15/19
6A	0.32	0.55	49	20 or 13 + 5[f]	15/20	30[e]	15/19	10, 4 ft	15/19
7	0.32	0.55	49	20 or 13 + 5[f]	19/21	38[e]	15/19	10, 4 ft	15/19

a. *R*-values are minimums. *U*-factors are maximums. When insulation is installed in a cavity which is less than the label or design thickness of the insulation, the installed *R*-value of the insulation shall not be less than the *R*-values specified in the table.

b. The fenestration *U*-factor column excludes skylights.

c. "15/19" means R-15 continuous insulation on the interior or exterior of the home or R-19 cavity insulation at the interior of the basement wall. "15/19" may be met with R-13 cavity insulation on the interior of the basement wall plus R-5 continuous insulation on the interior or exterior of the home. "10/13" means R-10 continuous insulation on the interior or exterior of the home or R-13 cavity insulation at the interior of the basement wall.

d. R-5 shall be added to the required slab edge *R*-values for heated slabs.

e. Or insulation sufficient to fill the framing cavity, R-19 minimum.

f. First value is cavity insulation, second is continuous insulation or insulated siding, so "13 + 5" means R-13 cavity insulation plus R-5 continuous insulation or insulated siding. If structural sheathing covers 40% or less of the exterior, continuous insulation *R*-value may be reduced by no more than R-3 in the locations where structural sheathing is used – to maintain a consistent total sheathing thickness.

g. The second *R*-value applies when more than half the insulation is on the interior of the mass wall.

R 408.31063

TABLE R402.1.3
EQUIVALENT *U*-FACTORS[a]

CLIMATE ZONE	FENESTRATION *U*-FACTOR	SKYLIGHT *U*-FACTOR	CEILING *U*-FACTOR	FRAME WALL *U*-FACTOR	MASS WALL *U*-FACTOR[b]	FLOOR *U*-FACTOR	BASEMENT WALL *U*-FACTOR	CRAWL SPACE WALL *U*-FACTOR
5A	0.32	0.55	0.030	0.057	0.082	0.033	0.059	0.055
6A	0.32	0.55	0.026	0.057	0.060	0.033	0.050	0.055
7	0.32	0.55	0.026	0.057	0.057	0.028	0.050	0.055

a. Nonfenestration *U*-factors shall be obtained from measurement, calculation or an approved source.
b. When more than half the insulation is on the interior, the mass wall U-factors shall be a maximum of 0.065 in zone 5 and marine 4, and 0.057 in zones 6 and 7.

R 408.31065

R402.2.1 Ceilings with attic spaces. When Section R402.1.1 would require R-38 in the ceiling, R-30 shall be deemed to satisfy the requirement for R-38 wherever the full height of uncompressed R-30 insulation extends over the wall top plate at the eaves. Similarly, R-38 shall be deemed to satisfy the requirement for R-49 wherever the full height of uncompressed R-38 insulation extends over the wall top plate at the eaves. This reduction shall not apply to the *U*-factor alternative approach in Section R402.1.3 and the total UA alternative in Section R402.1.4.

R402.2.2 Ceilings without attic spaces. Where Section R402.1.1 would require insulation levels above R-30 and the design of the roof/ceiling assembly does not allow sufficient space for the required insulation, the minimum required insulation for such roof/ceiling assemblies shall be R-30. This reduction of insulation from the requirements of Section R402.1.1 shall be limited to 500 square feet (46 m²) or 20 percent of the total insulated ceiling area, whichever is less. This reduction shall not apply to the *U*-factor alternative approach in Section R402.1.3 and the total UA alternative in Section R402.1.4.

R402.2.3 Eave baffle. For air permeable insulations in vented attics, a baffle shall be installed adjacent to soffit and eave vents. Baffles shall maintain an opening equal or greater than the size of the vent. The baffle shall extend over the top of the attic insulation. The baffle shall be permitted to be any solid material.

R402.2.4 Access hatches and doors. Access doors from conditioned spaces to unconditioned spaces (e.g., attics and crawl spaces) shall be weatherstripped and insulated to a level equivalent to the insulation on the surrounding surfaces. Access shall be provided to all equipment that prevents damaging or compressing the insulation. A wood framed or equivalent baffle or retainer is required to be provided when loose fill insulation is installed, the purpose of which is to prevent the loose fill insulation from spilling into the living space when the attic access is opened, and to provide a permanent means of maintaining the installed *R*-value of the loose fill insulation.

R402.2.5 Mass walls. Mass walls for the purposes of this chapter shall be considered above-grade walls of concrete block, concrete, insulated concrete form (ICF), masonry cavity, brick (other than brick veneer), earth (adobe, compressed earth block, rammed earth) and solid timber/logs.

R402.2.6 Steel-frame ceilings, walls, and floors. Steel-frame ceilings, walls, and floors shall meet the insulation requirements of Table R402.2.6 or shall meet the *U*-factor requirements in Table R402.1.3. The calculation of the *U*-factor for a steel-frame envelope assembly shall use a series-parallel path calculation method.

R 408.31070

R402.2.7 Floors. Floor insulation shall be installed to maintain permanent contact with the underside of the sub-floor decking.

R402.2.8 Basement walls. Walls associated with conditioned basements shall be insulated from the top of the *basement wall* down to 10 feet (3048 mm) below grade or to the basement floor, whichever is less. Walls associated with unconditioned basements shall meet this requirement unless the floor overhead is insulated in accordance with Sections R402.1.1 and R402.2.7.

R402.2.9 Slab-on-grade floors. Slab-on-grade floors with a floor surface less than 12 inches (305 mm) below grade shall be insulated in accordance with Table R402.1.1. The insulation shall extend downward from the top of the slab on the outside or inside of the foundation wall. Insulation located below grade shall be extended the distance provided in Table R402.1.1 by any combination of vertical insulation, insulation extending under the slab or insulation extending out from the building. Insulation extending away from the building shall be protected by pavement or by a minimum of 10 inches (254 mm) of soil. The top edge of the insulation installed between the *exterior wall* and the edge of the interior slab shall be permitted to be cut at a 45-degree (0.79 rad) angle away from the *exterior wall*. Slab-edge insulation is not required in jurisdictions designated by the *building official* as having a very heavy termite infestation.

R402.2.10 Crawl space walls. As an alternative to insulating floors over crawl spaces, crawl space walls shall be permitted to be insulated when the crawl space is not vented to the outside. Crawl space wall insulation shall be permanently fastened to the wall and extend downward from the floor to the finished grade level and then vertically and/or horizontally for at least an additional 24 inches (610 mm). Exposed earth in unvented crawl space foundations shall be covered with a continuous Class I vapor retarder in accordance with this code. All joints of the vapor retarder shall overlap by 6 inches (153 mm) and be sealed or taped. The edges of the vapor retarder shall extend at least 6 inches (153 mm) up the stem wall and shall be attached to the stem wall.

TABLE R402.2.6
STEEL-FRAME CEILING, WALL AND FLOOR INSULATION
(R-VALUE)

WOOD FRAME R-VALUE REQUIREMENT	COLD-FORMED STEEL EQUIVALENT R-VALUE[a]
Steel Truss Ceilings[b]	
R-30	R-38 or R-30 + 3 or R-26 + 5
R-38	R-49 or R-38 + 3
R-49	R-38 + 5
Steel Joist Ceilings[b]	
R-30	R-38 in 2 × 4 or 2 × 6 or 2 × 8 R-49 in any framing
R-38	R-49 in 2 × 4 or 2 × 6 or 2 × 8 or 2 × 10
Steel-Framed Wall, 16″ o.c.	
R-13	R-13 + 4.2 or R-19 + 2.1 or R-21 + 2.8 or R-0 + 9.3 or R-15 + 3.8 or R-21 + 3.1
R-13 + 3	R-0 + 11.2 or R-13 + 6.1 or R-15 + 5.7 or R-19 + 5.0 or R-21 + 4.7
R-20	R-0 + 14.0 or R-13 + 8.9 or R-15 + 8.5 or R-19 + 7.8 or R-19 + 6.2 or R-21 + 7.5
R-20 + 5	R-13 + 12.7 or R-15 + 12.3 or R-19 + 11.6 or R-21 + 11.3 or R-25 + 10.9
R-21	R-0 + 14.6 or R-13 + 9.5 or R-15 + 9.1 or R-19 + 8.4 or R-21 + 8.1 or R-25 + 7.7
Steel-Framed Wall, 24″ o.c.	
R-13	R-0 + 9.3 or R-13 + 3.0 or R-15 + 2.4
R-13 + 3	R-0 + 11.2 or R-13 + 4.9 or R-15 + 4.3 or R-19 + 3.5 or R-21 + 3.1
R-20	R-0 + 14.0 or R-13 + 7.7 or R-15 + 7.1 or R-19 + 6.3 or R-21 + 5.9
R-20 + 5	R-13 + 11.5 or R-15 + 10.9 or R-19 + 10.1 or R-21 + 9.7 or R-25 + 9.1
R-21	R-0 + 14.6 or R-13 + 8.3 or R-15 + 7.7 or R-19 + 6.9 or R-21 + 6.5 or R-25 + 5.9
Steel Joist Floor	
R-13	R-19 in 2 × 6, or R-19 + 6 in 2 × 8 or 2 × 10
R-19	R-19 + 6 in 2 × 6, or R-19 + 12 in 2 × 8 or 2 × 10

a. Cavity insulation R-value is listed first, followed by continuous insulation R-value.
b. Insulation exceeding the height of the framing shall cover the framing.

R402.2.11 Masonry veneer. Insulation shall not be required on the horizontal portion of the foundation that supports a masonry veneer.

R402.2.12 Thermally isolated sunroom insulation. The minimum ceiling insulation R-values shall be R-24 in zones 5 to 7. The minimum wall R-value shall be R-13 in all zones. New wall or walls separating a sunroom from conditioned space shall meet the building thermal envelope requirements.

R 408.31063a

R402.3 Fenestration (Prescriptive). In addition to the requirements of Section R402, fenestration shall comply with Sections R402.3.1 through R402.3.6.

R402.3.1 U-factor. An area-weighted aver- age of fenestration products shall be permitted to satisfy the U-factor requirements.

R402.3.3 Glazed fenestration exemption. Up to 15 square feet (1.4 m²) of glazed fenestration per dwelling unit may be exempt from U-factor requirements in Section R402.1.1. This exemption shall not apply to the U-factor alternative approach in Section R402.1.3 and the total UA alternative in Section R402.1.4.

R 408.301064

R402.3.4 Opaque door exemption. One side- hinged opaque door assembly up to 24 square feet (2.22 m²) in area is exempted from the U-factor requirement in Section R402.1.1. This exemption shall not apply to the U-factor alternative approach in Section R402.1.3 and the total UA alternative in Section R402.1.4.

R402.3.5 Sunroom U-factor. All *sunrooms* enclosing conditioned spaces shall meet the fenestration require- ments of this code.

Exception: For *sunrooms* with *thermal isolation* and enclosing conditioned spaces, in Zones 4 through 8, the following exceptions to the fenestration requirements of this code shall apply:

1. The maximum fenestration U-factor shall be 0.45; and

2. The maximum skylight U-factor shall be 0.70. New fenestration separating the *sunroom* with *thermal isolation* from *conditioned space* shall meet the *building thermal envelope* requirements of this code.

R402.3.6 Replacement fenestration. Where some or all of an existing fenestration unit is replaced with a new fen- estration product, including sash and glazing, the replace- ment fenestration unit shall meet the applicable requirements for U-factor in Table R402.1.3. Where some or all of an existing fenestration unit is replaced with a new fenestration product, including sash and glazing, the replacement fenestration unit shall meet the applicable requirements for U-factor in Table R402.1.1.

R 408.301064

R402.4 Air leakage. The building thermal envelope shall be constructed to limit air leakage in accordance with the require- ments of Sections R402.4.1 through R402.4.4.

R 408.31069

R402.4.1 Building thermal envelope. The building ther- mal envelope shall comply with Sections R402.4.1.1 and R402.4.1.2.

R 408.31069

R402.4.1.1 Installation (mandatory). The compo- nents of the building thermal envelope as listed in Table R402.4.1.1 shall be installed in accordance with the manufacturer's instructions and the criteria listed in

Table R402.4.1.1, as applicable to the method of construction. The sealing methods between dissimilar materials shall allow for differential expansion and contraction.

R 408.31069

R402.4.1.2 Testing (prescriptive). The building or dwelling unit shall be tested and verified as having an air leakage rate of not exceeding 4 air changes per hour. Testing shall be conducted with a blower door at a pressure of 0.2 inches w.g. (50 pascals). Where required by the code official, testing shall be conducted by a certified independent third party. Certification programs shall be approved by the state construction code commission. A written report of the results of the test shall be signed by the party conducting the test and provided to the code official. Testing shall be performed at any time after creation of all penetrations of the building thermal envelope. During testing:

1. Exterior windows and doors, fireplace and stove doors shall be closed, but not sealed, beyond the intended weatherstripping or other infiltration control measures;

2. Dampers including exhaust, intake, makeup air, backdraft and flue dampers shall be closed, but not sealed beyond intended infiltration control measures;

3. Interior doors, if installed at the time of the test, shall be open;

4. Exterior doors for continuous ventilation systems and heat recovery ventilators shall be closed and sealed;

5. Heating and cooling systems, if installed at the time of the test, shall be turned off; and

6. Supply and return registers, if installed at the time of the test, shall be fully open.

R 408.31069

R402.4.2 Fireplaces (mandatory). New wood-burning masonry fireplaces shall have tight-fitting flue dampers and outdoor combustion air.

R 408.31069

R402.4.3 Fenestration air leakage (mandatory). Windows, skylights, and sliding glass doors shall have an air infiltration rate of no more than 0.3 cfm per square foot (1.5 L/s/m^2), and swinging doors no more than 0.5 cfm per square foot (2.6 L/s/m^2), when tested according to NFRC 400 or AAMA/WDMA/CSA 101/I.S.2/A440 by an accredited, independent laboratory and listed and labeled by the manufacturer.

Exception: Site-built windows, skylights, and doors.

R 408.31069

R402.4.4 Recessed lighting (mandatory). Recessed luminaires installed in the building thermal envelope shall be sealed to limit air leakage between conditioned and unconditioned spaces. All recessed luminaires shall be IC-rated and labeled as having an air leakage rate not more than 2.0 cfm (0.944 L/s) when tested in accordance with ASTM E283 at a 1.57 psf (75 Pa) pressure differential. All recessed luminaires shall be sealed with a gasket or caulk between the housing and the interior wall or ceiling covering.

R 408.31069

R402.5 Maximum fenestration *U*-factor and SHGC (Mandatory). The area-weighted average maximum fenestration *U*-factor permitted using tradeoffs from Section R402.1.4 or R405 shall be 0.48 in Zones 4 and 5 and 0.40 in Zones 6 through 8 for vertical fenestration, and 0.75 in Zones 4 through 8 for skylights. The area-weighted average maximum fenestration SHGC permitted using tradeoffs from Section R405 in Zones 1 through 3 shall be 0.50.

SECTION R403
SYSTEMS

R403.1 Controls (Mandatory). At least one thermostat shall be provided for each separate heating and cooling system.

R403.1.1 Programmable thermostat. Where the primary heating system is a forced-air furnace, at least one thermostat per dwelling unit shall be capable of controlling the heating and cooling system on a daily schedule to maintain different temperature set points at different times of the day. This thermostat shall include the capability to set back or temporarily operate the system to maintain zone temperatures down to 55°F (13°C) or up to 85°F (29°C). The thermostat shall initially be programmed with a heating temperature set point no higher than 70°F (21°C) and a cooling temperature set point no lower than 78°F (26°C).

R403.1.2 Heat pump supplementary heat (Mandatory). Heat pumps having supplementary electric-resistance heat shall have controls that, except during defrost, prevent supplemental heat operation when the heat pump compressor can meet the heating load.

R403.2 Ducts. Ducts and air handlers shall be in accordance with Sections R403.2.1 through R403.2.3.

R403.2.1 Insulation (prescriptive). All portions of the air distribution system shall be installed in accordance with Section M1601 and be insulated to an installed R-6 when system components are located within the building but outside the conditioned space, and R-8 when located outside to the building thermal envelope. When located within a building envelope assembly, at least R-8 shall be applied between the duct and that portion of the assembly farthest from conditioned space.

Exception: Portions of the air distribution system within appliances or equipment.

R 408.31066

TABLE R402.4.1.1
AIR BARRIER AND INSULATION INSTALLATION

COMPONENT	CRITERIA[a]
Air barrier and thermal barrier	A continuous air barrier shall be installed in the building envelope. Exterior thermal envelope contains a continuous air barrier. Breaks or joints in the air barrier shall be sealed. Air-permeable insulation shall not be used as a sealing material.
Ceiling/attic	The air barrier in any dropped ceiling/soffit shall be aligned with the insulation and any gaps in the air barrier sealed. Access openings, drop down stair, or knee wall doors to unconditioned attic spaces shall be sealed.
Walls	Corners and headers shall be insulated and the junction of the foundation and sill plate shall be sealed. The junction of the top plate and top of exterior walls shall be sealed. Exterior thermal envelope insulation for framed walls shall be installed in substantial contact and continuous alignment with the air barrier. Knee walls shall be sealed.
Windows, skylights and doors	The space between window/door jambs and framing, and skylights and framing shall be sealed.
Rim joists	Rim joists shall be insulated and include the air barrier.
Floors (including above-garage and cantilevered floors)	Insulation shall be installed to maintain permanent contact with underside of subfloor decking. The air barrier shall be installed at any exposed edge of insulation.
Crawl space walls	Where provided in lieu of floor insulation, insulation shall be permanently attached to the crawlspace walls. Exposed earth in unvented crawl spaces shall be covered with a Class I vapor retarder with overlapping joints taped.
Shafts, penetrations	Duct shafts, utility penetrations, and flue shafts opening to exterior or unconditioned space shall be sealed.
Narrow cavities	Batts in narrow cavities shall be cut to fit, or narrow cavities shall be filled by insulation that on installation readily conforms to the available cavity space.
Garage separation	Air sealing shall be provided between the garage and conditioned spaces.
Recessed lighting	Recessed light fixtures installed in the building thermal envelope shall be air tight, IC rated, and sealed to the drywall.
Plumbing and wiring	Batt insulation shall be cut neatly to fit around wiring and plumbing in exterior walls, or insulation that on installation readily conforms to available space shall extend behind piping and wiring.
Shower/tub on exterior wall	Exterior walls adjacent to showers and tubs shall be insulated and the air barrier installed separating them from the showers and tubs.
Electrical/phone box on exterior walls	The air barrier shall be installed behind electrical or communication boxes or air-sealed boxes shall be installed.
HVAC register boots	HVAC register boots that penetrate building thermal envelope shall be sealed to the subfloor or drywall.
Fireplace	An air barrier shall be installed on fireplace walls.

a. In addition, inspection of log walls shall be in accordance with the provisions of ICC-400.

R 408.31069

R403.2.2 Sealing (mandatory). Ducts, air handlers, and filter boxes shall be sealed. Joints and seams shall comply with either the *International Mechanical Code* or *International Residential Code*, as applicable.

Exceptions:

1. Air-impermeable spray foam products may be applied without additional joint seals.

2. Where a duct connection is made that is partially inaccessible, 3 screws or rivets shall be equally spaced on the exposed portion of the joint so as to prevent a hinge effect.

3. Continuously welded and locking-type longitudinal joints and seams in ducts operating at static pressures less than 2 inches (51 mm) of water column (500 Pa) pressure classification shall not require additional closure systems.

Duct tightness shall be verified by either of the following:

1. Postconstruction test: Total leakage to the outside of a conditioned space or total leakage shall be less than or equal to 4 cfm (113.3 L/min) per 100 square feet (9.29 m²) of conditioned floor area when tested at a pressure differential of 0.1 inches (2.54 mm) w.g. (25 Pa) across the entire system, including the manufacturer's air handler enclosure. All register

boots shall be taped or otherwise sealed during the test.

2. Rough-in test: Total leakage shall be less than or equal to 4 cfm (113.3 L/min) per 100 square feet (9.29 m²) of conditioned floor area when tested at a pressure differential of 0.1 inches (2.54 mm) w.g. (25 Pa) across the system, including the manufacturer's air handler enclosure. All registers shall be taped or otherwise sealed during the test. If the air handler is not installed at the time of the test, total leakage shall be less than or equal to 3 cfm (85 L/min) per 100 square feet (9.29 m²) of conditioned floor area.

> **Exception:** The total leakage test is not required for ducts and air handlers located entirely within the building thermal envelope.

R 408.31066

R403.2.2.1 Sealed air handler. Air handlers shall have a manufacturer's designation for an air leakage of no more than 2 percent of the design air flow rate when tested in accordance with ASHRAE 193.

R403.2.3 Building cavities (Mandatory). Building framing cavities shall not be used as ducts or plenums.

R403.3 Mechanical system piping insulation (Mandatory). Mechanical system piping capable of carrying fluids above 105°F (41°C) or below 55°F (13°C) shall be insulated to a minimum of R-3.

R403.3.1 Protection of piping insulation. Piping insulation exposed to weather shall be protected from damage, including that caused by sunlight, moisture, equipment maintenance, and wind, and shall provide shielding from solar radiation that can cause degradation of the material. Adhesive tape shall not be permitted.

R403.4 Service hot water systems. Energy conservation measures for service hot water systems shall be in accordance with Sections R403.4.1 and R403.4.2.

R403.4.1 Circulating hot water systems (Mandatory). All circulating service hot water piping shall be insulated to at least R-2. Circulating hot water systems shall include an automatic or readily accessible manual switch that can turn off the hot water circulating pump when the system is not in use.

Exceptions:

1. Factory-installed piping within HVAC equipment tested and rated in accordance with a test procedure referenced by this code.

2. Runout piping not exceeding 4 feet (1219 mm) in length and 1 inch (25 mm) in diameter between the control valve and HVAC coil.

R 408.31066

R403.4.2 Hot water pipe insulation (prescriptive). Insulation for hot water pipe with a minimum thermal resistance (R-value) of R-3 shall be applied to the following:

1. Piping larger than $^3/_4$ inch (19.05 mm) nominal diameter.

2. Piping serving more than 1 dwelling unit.

3. Piping located outside the conditioned space.

4. Piping from the water heater to a distribution manifold.

5. Piping located under a floor slab.

6. Buried piping.

7. Supply and return piping in recirculation systems other than demand recirculation systems.

R 408.31066

TABLE R403.4.2
MAXIMUM RUN LENGTH (feet)[a]

Nominal pipe diameter of largest diameter pipe in the run (inch)	$^3/_8$	$^1/_2$	$^3/_4$	$> ^3/_4$
Maximum run length	30	20	10	5

For SI: 1 inch = 25.4 mm, 1 foot = 304.8 mm.

a. Total length of all piping from the distribution manifold or the recirculation loop to a point of use.

R403.5 Mechanical ventilation (Mandatory). The building shall be provided with ventilation that meets the requirements of Section M1507 of the *Michigan Residential Code* or the *International Mechanical Code*, as applicable, or with other approved means of ventilation. Outdoor air intakes and exhausts shall have automatic or gravity dampers that close when the ventilation system is not operating.

R403.5.1 Whole-house mechanical ventilation system fan efficacy. Mechanical ventilation system fans shall meet the efficacy requirements of Table R403.5.1.

> **Exception:** Where mechanical ventilation fans are integral to tested and listed HVAC equipment, they shall be powered by an electronically commutated motor.

R403.6 Equipment sizing (Mandatory). Heating and cooling equipment shall be sized in accordance with ACCA Manual S based on building loads calculated in accordance with ACCA Manual J or other *approved* heating and cooling calculation methodologies.

TABLE R403.5.1
MECHANICAL VENTILATION SYSTEM FAN EFFICACY

FAN LOCATION	AIR FLOW RATE MINIMUM (CFM)	MINIMUM EFFICACY (CFM/WATT)	AIR FLOW RATE MAXIMUM (CFM)
Range hoods	Any	2.8 cfm/watt	Any
In-line fan	Any	2.8 cfm/watt	Any
Bathroom, utility room	10	1.4 cfm/watt	< 90
Bathroom, utility room	90	2.8 cfm/watt	Any

For SI: 1 cubic foot per minute = 28.3 L/min.

R403.7 Systems serving multiple dwelling units (Mandatory). Systems serving multiple dwelling units shall comply with Sections C403 and C404 of the IECC—Commercial Provisions in lieu of Section R403.

R403.8 Snow melt system controls (Mandatory). Snow- and ice-melting systems, supplied through energy service to the building, shall include automatic controls capable of shutting off the system when the pavement temperature is above 50°F (10°C), and no precipitation is falling and an automatic or manual control that will allow shutoff when the outdoor temperature is above 40°F (4.8°C).

R403.9 Pools and inground permanently installed spas (Mandatory). Pools and inground permanently installed spas shall comply with Sections R403.9.1 through R403.9.3.

R403.9.1 Heaters. All heaters shall be equipped with a readily *accessible* on-off switch that is mounted outside of the heater to allow shutting off the heater without adjusting the thermostat setting. Gas-fired heaters shall not be equipped with constant burning pilot lights.

R403.9.2 Time switches. Time switches or other control method that can automatically turn off and on heaters and pumps according to a preset schedule shall be installed on all heaters and pumps. Heaters, pumps and motors that have built in timers shall be deemed in compliance with this requirement.

Exceptions:

1. Where public health standards require 24-hour pump operation.

2. Where pumps are required to operate solar-and waste-heat-recovery pool heating systems.

R403.9.3 Covers. Heated pools and inground permanently installed spas shall be provided with a vapor-retardant cover.

Exception: Pools deriving over 70 percent of the energy for heating from site-recovered energy, such as a heat pump or solar energy source computed over an operating season.

SECTION R404
ELECTRICAL POWER AND LIGHTING SYSTEMS (MANDATORY)

R404.1 Lighting equipment (Mandatory). A minimum of 75 percent of the lamps in permanently installed lighting fixtures shall be high-efficacy lamps or a minimum of 75 percent of the permanently installed lighting fixtures shall contain only high-efficacy lamps.

Exception: Low-voltage lighting shall not be required to utilize high-efficiency lamps.

R404.1.1 Lighting equipment (Mandatory). Fuel gas lighting systems shall not have continuously burning pilot lights.

SECTION R405
SIMULATED PERFORMANCE ALTERNATIVE (PERFORMANCE)

R405.1 Scope. This section establishes criteria for compliance using simulated energy performance analysis. Such analysis shall include heating, cooling, and service water heating energy only.

R405.2 Mandatory requirements. Compliance with this section requires that the mandatory provisions identified in Section R401.15 be met. All supply and return ducts not completely inside the *building thermal envelope* shall be insulated to a minimum of R-6.

R405.3 Performance-based compliance. Compliance based on simulated energy performance requires that a proposed residence (*proposed design*) be shown to have an annual energy cost that is less than or equal to the annual energy cost of the *standard reference design*. Energy prices shall be taken from a source *approved* by the *building official*, such as the Department of Energy, Energy Information Administration's *State Energy Price and Expenditure Report*. *Building officials* shall be permitted to require time-of-use pricing in energy cost calculations.

Exception: The energy use based on source energy expressed in Btu (J) or Btu per square foot (J/m²) of *conditioned floor area* shall be permitted to be substituted for the energy cost. The source energy multiplier for electricity shall be 3.16. The source energy multiplier for fuels other than electricity shall be 1.1.

R405.4 Documentation. Documentation of the software used for the performance design and the parameters for the building shall be in accordance with Sections R405.4.1 through R405.4.3.

R405.4.1 Compliance software tools. Documentation verifying that the methods and accuracy of the compliance software tools conform to the provisions of this section shall be provided to the *building official*.

R405.4.2 Compliance report. Compliance software tools shall generate a report that documents that the *proposed design* complies with Section R405.3. The compliance documentation shall include the following information:

1. Address or other identification of the residence;

2. An inspection checklist documenting the building component characteristics of the *proposed design* as listed in Table R405.5.2(1). The inspection checklist shall show results for both the *standard reference design* and the *proposed design*, and shall document all inputs entered by the user necessary to reproduce the results;

3. Name of individual completing the compliance report; and

4. Name and version of the compliance software tool.

Exception: Multiple orientations. When an otherwise identical building model is offered in multiple orientations, compliance for any orientation shall be permitted by documenting that the building meets the performance requirements in each of the four cardinal (north, east, south and west) orientations.

R405.4.3 Additional documentation. The *building official* shall be permitted to require the following documents:

1. Documentation of the building component characteristics of the *standard reference design.*

2. A certification signed by the builder providing the building component characteristics of the *proposed design* as given in Table R405.5.2(1).

3. Documentation of the actual values used in the software calculations for the *proposed design.*

R405.5 Calculation procedure. Calculations of the performance design shall be in accordance with Sections R405.5.1 and R405.5.2.

R405.5.1 General. Except as specified by this section, the *standard reference design* and *proposed design* shall be configured and analyzed using identical methods and techniques.

R405.5.2 Residence specifications. The *standard reference design* and *proposed design* shall be configured and analyzed as specified by Table R405.5.2(1). Table R405.5.2(1) shall include by reference all notes contained in Table R402.1.1.

R405.6 Calculation software tools. Calculation software, where used, shall be in accordance with Sections R405.6.1 through R405.6.3.

R405.6.1 Minimum capabilities. Calculation procedures used to comply with this section shall be software tools capable of calculating the annual energy consumption of all building elements that differ between the *standard reference design* and the *proposed design* and shall include the following capabilities:

1. Computer generation of the *standard reference design* using only the input for the *proposed design.* The calculation procedure shall not allow the user to directly modify the building component characteristics of the *standard reference design.*

2. Calculation of whole-building (as a single *zone*) sizing for the heating and cooling equipment in the *standard reference design* residence in accordance with Section R403.6.

3. Calculations that account for the effects of indoor and outdoor temperatures and part-load ratios on the performance of heating, ventilating and air-conditioning equipment based on climate and equipment sizing.

4. Printed *building official* inspection checklist listing each of the *proposed design* component characteristics from Table R405.5.2(1) determined by the analysis to provide compliance, along with their respective performance ratings (e.g., *R*-value, *U*-factor, SHGC, HSPF, AFUE, SEER, EF, etc.).

R405.6.2 Specific approval. Performance analysis tools meeting the applicable sections of Section R405 shall be permitted to be *approved.* Tools are permitted to be *approved* based on meeting a specified threshold for a jurisdiction. The *building official* shall be permitted to approve tools for a specified application or limited scope.

R405.6.3 Input values. When calculations require input values not specified by Sections R402, R403, R404 and R405, those input values shall be taken from an *approved* source.

SECTION R406
ENERGY RATING INDEX
COMPLIANCE ALTERNATIVE

R406.1 Scope. This section establishes criteria for compliance using an energy rating index (ERI) analysis.

R 408.31071a

R406.2 Mandatory requirements. Compliance with this section requires that the mandatory provisions identified in Sections R401.2 and R403.4.2 be met. The building thermal envelope shall be greater than or equal to levels of efficiency and solar heat gain coefficient in Table 402.1.2 or 402.1.4 of the 2009 *International Energy Conservation Code.*

> **Exception:** Supply and return ducts not completely inside the building thermal envelope shall be insulated to a minimum of R-6.

R 408.31071a

R406.3 Energy rating index. The energy rating index (ERI) shall be a numerical integer value that is based on a linear scale constructed such that the ERI reference design has an index value of 100 and a residential building that uses no net purchased energy has an index value of 0. Each integer value on the scale shall represent a 1% change in the total energy use of the rated design relative to the total energy use of the ERI reference design. The ERI shall consider all energy used in the residential building.

R 408.31071a

R406.3.1 ERI reference design. The ERI reference design shall be configured such that it meets the minimum requirements of the 2006 *International Energy Conservation Code* prescriptive requirements.

The proposed residential building shall be shown to have an annual total normalized modified load less than or equal to the annual total loads of the ERI reference design.

R 08.31071a

R406.4 ERI-based compliance. Compliance based on an ERI analysis requires that the rated design be shown to have an ERI less than or equal to the appropriate value listed in Table R406.4 when compared to the ERI reference design.

R 408.31071a

TABLE R406.4
MAXIMUM ENERGY RATING INDEX

CLIMATE ZONE	ENERGY RATING INDEX
1	52
2	52
3	51
4	54
5	55
6	54
7	53
8	53

R 408.31071a

R406.5 Verification by approved agency. Verification of compliance with Section R406 shall be completed by an approved third party.

R 408.31071a

R406.6 Documentation. Documentation of the software used to determine the ERI and the parameters for the residential building shall be in accordance with Sections R406.6.1 through R406.6.3.

R 408.31071a

R406.6.1 Compliance software tools. Documentation verifying that the methods and accuracy of the compliance software tools conform to the provisions of this section shall be provided to the code official.

R 408.31071a

R406.6.2 Compliance report. Compliance software tools shall generate a report that documents that the ERI of the rated design complies with Sections R406.3 and R406.4. The compliance documentation shall include the following information:

1. Address or other identification of the residential building.

2. An inspection checklist documenting the building component characteristics of the rated design. The inspection checklist shall show results for both the ERI reference design and the rated design, and shall document all inputs entered by the user necessary to reproduce the results.

3. Name of individual completing the compliance report.

4. Name and version of the compliance software tool.

Exception: Multiple orientations. Where an otherwise identical building model is offered in multiple orientations, compliance for any orientation shall be permitted by documenting that the building meets the performance requirements in each of the 4 (north, east, south and west) cardinal orientations.

R 408.31071a

R406.6.3 Additional documentation. The code official may require the following documents:

1. Documentation of the building component characteristics of the ERI reference design.

2. A certification signed by the builder providing the building component characteristics of the rated design.

3. Documentation of the actual values used in the software calculations for the rated design.

R 408.31071a

R406.7 Calculation software tools. Calculation software, where used, shall be in accordance with Sections R406.7.1 through R406.7.3.

R 408.31071a

R406.7.1 Minimum capabilities. Calculation procedures used to comply with this section shall be software tools capable of calculating the ERI as described in Section N1106.3, and shall include the following capabilities:

1. Computer generation of the ERI reference design using only the input for the rated design.

   The calculation procedure shall not allow the user to directly modify the building component characteristics of the ERI reference design.

2. Calculation of whole-building, as single zone, sizing for the heating and cooling equipment in the ERI reference design residence in accordance with Section R403.7.

3. Calculations that account for the effects of indoor and outdoor temperatures and part-load ratios on the performance of heating, ventilating, and air-conditioning equipment based on climate and equipment sizing.

4. Printed code official inspection checklist listing each of the rated design component characteristics determined by the analysis to provide compliance, along with their respective performance ratings.

R 408.31071a

R406.7.2 Specific approval. Performance analysis tools meeting the applicable sections of Section R406 shall be approved. Tools are permitted to be approved based on meeting a specified threshold for a jurisdiction. The code official shall approve tools for a specified application or limited scope.

R 408.31071a

R406.7.3 Input values. When calculations require input values not specified by Sections R402, R403, R404, and R405, those input values shall be taken from an approved source.

R 408.31071a

TABLE R405.5.2(1)
SPECIFICATIONS FOR THE STANDARD REFERENCE AND PROPOSED DESIGNS

BUILDING COMPONENT	STANDARD REFERENCE DESIGN	PROPOSED DESIGN
Above-grade walls	Type: mass wall if proposed wall is mass; otherwise wood frame. Gross area: same as proposed U-factor: from Table R402.1.3 Solar absorptance = 0.75 Remittance = 0.90	As proposed As proposed As proposed As proposed As proposed
Basement and crawl space walls	Type: same as proposed Gross area: same as proposed U-factor: from Table R402.1.3, with insulation layer on interior side of walls.	As proposed As proposed As proposed
Above-grade floors	Type: wood frame Gross area: same as proposed U-factor: from Table R402.1.3	As proposed As proposed As proposed
Ceilings	Type: wood frame Gross area: same as proposed U-factor: from Table R402.1.3	As proposed As proposed As proposed
Roofs	Type: composition shingle on wood sheathing Gross area: same as proposed Solar absorptance = 0.75 Emittance = 0.90	As proposed As proposed As proposed As proposed
Attics	Type: vented with aperture = 1 ft² per 300 ft² ceiling area	As proposed
Foundations	Type: same as proposed foundation wall area above and below grade and soil. Characteristics: same as proposed.	As proposed As proposed
Doors	Area: 40 ft² Orientation: North U-factor: same as fenestration from Table R402.1.3.	As proposed As proposed As proposed
Glazing[a]	Total area[b] = (a) The proposed glazing area: where proposed glazing area is less than 15% of the conditioned floor area. (b) 15% of the conditioned floor area: where the proposed glazing area is 15% or more of the conditioned floor area. Orientation: equally distributed to 4 cardinal compass orientations (N, E, S & W). U-factor: from Table R402.1.3 SHGC: From Table R402.1.1 except that for climates with no requirement (NR) SHGC = 0.40 shall be used. Interior shade fraction: 0.92-(0.21 × SHGC for the standard reference design) External shading: none	As proposed As proposed As proposed As proposed 0.92-(0.21 × SHGC as proposed) As proposed
Skylights	None	As proposed
Thermally isolated sunrooms	None	As proposed

(continued)

TABLE R405.5.2(1)—continued
SPECIFICATIONS FOR THE STANDARD REFERENCE AND PROPOSED DESIGNS

BUILDING COMPONENT	STANDARD REFERENCE DESIGN	PROPOSED DESIGN
Air exchange rate	Air leakage rate 4 of air changes per hour at a pressure of 0.2 inches w.g (50 Pa). The mechanical ventilation rate shall be in addition to the air leakage rate and the same as in the proposed design, but no greater than $0.01 \times CFA + 7.5 \times (N_{br} + 1)$ where: CFA = conditioned floor area N_{br} = number of bedrooms Energy recovery shall not be assumed for mechanical ventilation.	The measured air exchange rate[c]. The mechanical ventilation rate[d] shall be in addition to the air leakage rate and shall be as proposed.
Mechanical ventilation	None, except where mechanical ventilation is specified by the proposed design, in which case: kWh/yr = $0.03942 \times CFA + 29.565 \times (N_{br} + 1)$ where: CFA = conditioned floor area N_{br} + number of bedrooms	As proposed
Internal gains	IGain = $17,900 + 23.8 \times CFA + 4104 \times N_{br}$ (Btu/day per dwelling unit)	Same as standard reference design.
Internal mass	An internal mass for furniture and contents of 8 pounds per square foot of floor area.	Same as standard reference design, plus any additional mass specifically designed as a thermal storage element[c] but not integral to the building envelope or structure.
Structural mass	For masonry floor slabs, 80% of floor area covered by R-2 carpet and pad, and 20% of floor directly exposed to room air. For masonry basement walls, as proposed, but with insulation required by Table R402.1.3 located on the interior side of the walls. For other walls, for ceilings, floors, and interior walls, wood frame construction.	As proposed As proposed As proposed
Heating systems[f, g]	As proposed for other than electric heating without a heat pump. Where the proposed design utilizes electric heating without a heat pump the standard reference design shall be an air source heat pump meeting the requirements of the Michigan energy code—commercial provisions. Capacity: sized in accordance with Section R403.6.	As proposed
Cooling systems[f, h]	As proposed Capacity: sized in accordance with Section R403.6.	As proposed
Service water Heating[f, g, h, i]	As proposed Use: same as proposed design	As proposed gal/day = $30 + (10 \times N_{br})$
Thermal distribution systems	Untested distribution systems: DSE = 0.88 Tested Ducts: Leakage rate to outside conditioned space as specified in Section R403.3.2 Tested duct location: Unconditioned attic Tested duct insulation: in accordance with Section R403.2.1.	Untested distribution systems: DSE from Table R405.5.2(2) Tested ducts: Tested leakage rate to outside conditioned space Duct location: As proposed Duct insulation: As proposed
Thermostat	Type: Manual, cooling temperature setpoint = 75°F; Heating temperature setpoint = 72°F	Same as standard reference

(continued)

TABLE R405.5.2(1)—continued
SPECIFICATIONS FOR THE STANDARD REFERENCE AND PROPOSED DESIGNS

For SI: 1 square foot = 0.93 m², 1 British thermal unit = 1055 J, 1 pound per square foot = 4.88 kg/m², 1 gallon (U.S.) = 3.785 L, °C = (°F - 3)/1.8, 1 degree = 0.79 rad, 1 inch water gauge = 1250 Pa.

a. Glazing shall be defined as sunlight-transmitting fenestration, including the area of sash, curbing or other framing elements, that enclose conditioned space. Glazing includes the area of sunlight-transmitting fenestration assemblies in walls bounding conditioned basements. For doors where the sunlight-transmitting opening is less than 50% of the door area, the glazing area is the sunlight transmitting opening area. For all other doors, the glazing area is the rough frame opening area for the door including the door and the frame.

b. For residences with conditioned basements, R-2 and R-4 residences and townhouses, the following formula shall be used to determine glazing area:

$AF = A_s \times FA \times F$

where:

AF = Total glazing area.

A_s = Standard reference design total glazing area.

FA = (Above-grade thermal boundary gross wall area)/(above-grade boundary wall area + 0.5 × below-grade boundary wall area).

F = (Above-grade thermal boundary wall area)/(above-grade thermal boundary wall area + common wall area) or 0.56, whichever is greater.

and where:

Thermal boundary wall is any wall that separates conditioned space from unconditioned space or ambient conditions.

Above-grade thermal boundary wall is any thermal boundary wall component not in contact with soil.

Below-grade boundary wall is any thermal boundary wall in soil contact.

Common wall area is the area of walls shared with an adjoining dwelling unit.

L and CFA are in the same units.

c. Where required by the *code official,* testing shall be conducted by a certified independent third party. Hourly calculations as specified in the ASHRAE *Handbook of Fundamentals,* or the equivalent shall be used to determine the energy loads resulting from infiltration.

d. The combined air exchange rate for infiltration and mechanical ventilation shall be determined in accordance with equation 43 of 2001 ASHRAE *Handbook of Fundamentals,* page 26.24 and the "whole-house ventilation" provisions of 2001 ASHRAE *Handbook of Fundamentals,* page 26.19 for intermittent mechanical ventilation.

e. Thermal storage element shall mean a component not part of the floors, walls, or ceilings that is part of a passive solar system, and that provides thermal storage such as enclosed water columns, rock beds, or phase-change containers. A thermal storage element must be in the same room as fenestration that faces within 15 degrees (0.26 rad) of true south, or must be connected to such a room with pipes or ducts that allow the element to be actively charged.

f. For a proposed design with multiple heating, cooling or water heating systems using different fuel types, the applicable standard reference design system capacities and fuel types shall be weighted in accordance with their respective loads as calculated by accepted engineering practice for each equipment and fuel type present.

g. For a proposed design without a proposed heating system, a heating system with the prevailing federal minimum efficiency shall be assumed for both the standard reference and proposed design.

h. For a proposed design home without a proposed cooling system, an electric air conditioner with the prevailing federal minimum efficiency shall be assumed for both the standard reference design and the proposed design.

i. For a proposed design with a nonstorage-type water heater, a 40-gallon storage-type water heater with the prevailing federal minimum energy factor for the same fuel as the predominant heating fuel type shall be assumed. For the case of a proposed design without a proposed water heater, a 40-gallon storage-type water heater with the prevailing federal minimum efficiency for the same fuel as the predominant heating fuel type shall be assumed for both the proposed design and standard reference design.

R 408.31071

TABLE R405.5.2(2)
DEFAULT DISTRIBUTION SYSTEM EFFICIENCIES FOR PROPOSED DESIGNS[a]

DISTRIBUTION SYSTEM CONFIGURATION AND CONDITION	FORCED AIR SYSTEMS	HYDRONIC SYSTEMS[b]
Distribution system components located in unconditioned space	—	0.95
Untested distribution systems entirely located in conditioned space[c]	0.88	1
"Ductless" systems[d]	1	—

For SI: 1 cubic foot per minute = 0.47 L/s, 1 square foot = 0.093 m², 1 pound per square inch = 6895 Pa, 1 inch water gauge = 1250 Pa.

a. Default values given by this table are for untested distribution systems, which must still meet minimum requirements for duct system insulation.

b. Hydronic systems shall mean those systems that distribute heating and cooling energy directly to individual spaces using liquids pumped through closed-loop piping and that do not depend on ducted, forced airflow to maintain space temperatures.

c. Entire system in conditioned space shall mean that no component of the distribution system, including the air handler unit, is located outside of the conditioned space.

d. Ductless systems shall be allowed to have forced airflow across a coil but shall not have any ducted airflow external to the manufacturer's air handler enclosure.

INDEX